C000088264

# LAND DEGRADATION IN SOUTH ASIA:
# ITS SEVERITY, CAUSES AND EFFECTS
# UPON THE PEOPLE

FOOD AND AGRICULTURE ORGANIZATION OF THE UNITED NATIONS
Rome, 1994

M-51
ISBN 92-5-103595-4

# Contents

|                                                                          | Page |
|--------------------------------------------------------------------------|------|
| SUMMARY                                                                  | 1    |
| INTRODUCTION                                                             | 11   |
| Origin, objectives and constraints                                       | 11   |
| Origin of the study                                                      | 11   |
| Objectives                                                               | 12   |
| Constraints                                                              | 12   |
| Background to the South Asia region                                      | 13   |
| Land and population                                                      | 13   |
| Environment                                                              | 16   |
| Irrigation systems                                                       | 18   |
| Arrangement of the report                                                | 18   |
| TYPES OF LAND DEGRADATION                                                | 19   |
| Definitions                                                              | 19   |
| Types of land degradation assessed                                       | 20   |
| Other types of degradation included                                      | 21   |
| Types of degradation excluded from the study                             | 21   |
| Problems of the natural environment                                      | 22   |
| Reversible degradation and land reclamation                              | 22   |
| SOURCES OF DATA                                                          | 23   |
| Global Assessment of Soil Degradation (GLASOD)                           | 23   |
| Degrees of severity of degradation                                       | 24   |
| Data for South Asia                                                      | 25   |
| Treatment of Bhutan                                                      | 26   |
| The GLASOD assessment: results                                           | 27   |
| Other sources of data                                                    | 27   |
| Variations in data and the need for definition of degrees of severity    | 28   |

Page

STATUS OF DEGRADATION. I. EROSION AND FERTILITY DECLINE          29

Water erosion                                                    29
Wind erosion                                                     32
Soil fertility decline                                           35

The GLASOD estimate                                              35
Evidence for soil fertility decline                              35

STATUS OF DEGRADATION. II. OTHER TYPES OF DEGRADATION
AND SUMMARY                                                      37

Waterlogging                                                     39
Salinization                                                     41
Lowering of the groundwater table                               44
Other types of degradation                                      45

Deforestation and forest degradation                            45
Rangeland degradation                                           46

Watershed degradation and management                            47
Summary: the severity and extent of land degradation            47
Discussion                                                       52

CAUSES OF LAND DEGRADATION                                       55

Natural degradation hazards                                      56
Direct causes of degradation                                     57
Underlying causes of degradation                                 59
Land, population, poverty and degradation: the causal nexus      61

ECONOMIC CONSEQUENCES OF LAND DEGRADATION                        65

Introduction: economic and social consequences                  65
Economic valuation of natural resources and degradation          65

Concepts and approaches in natural resource accounting           65
Methods for the valuation of soil resources                      66
Provisional nature of these estimates                            67

Land degradation in South Asia: the orders of magnitude of the economic costs  69

Water erosion                                                    69
Wind erosion                                                     71
Soil fertility decline                                           71
Waterlogging                                                     72

  Page

    Salinization                                                    73
    Lowering of the water table                                     74

Macroeconomic impact of land degradation                                74

    Summary                                                         74
    The value of resources                                          75
    Discussion                                                      76

EFFECTS UPON THE PEOPLE                                                 77

Effects upon production                                                 77
Consequences for the people                                             79
Land degradation and the poor                                           80

INSTITUTIONS AND PROGRAMMES TO COMBAT DEGRADATION                       81

National institutions                                                   81

    Afghanistan                                                     81
    Bangladesh                                                      82
    Bhutan                                                          82
    India                                                           82
    Iran                                                            84
    Nepal                                                           84
    Pakistan                                                        85
    Sri Lanka                                                       85

National institutions: discussion                                       86
Environmental legislation                                               86
International institutions in the region                                87
Regional collaborative programmes                                       87

CONCLUSIONS AND PROPOSALS                                               89

Conclusions from the study                                              89
Proposals: introduction                                                 91
Proposals for strengthening efforts to combat land degradation          92

REFERENCES                                                              95

# List of tables

| | | Page |
|---|---|---|
| 1. | Land use in South Asia, 1990 | 15 |
| 2. | Land and population in South Asia, 1990 | 15 |
| 3. | Correspondence between GLASOD types of degradation and those of the present | 24 |
| 4. | GLASOD definitions of degrees of degradation | 24 |
| 5. | GLASOD assessment: areas affected by water erosion | 30 |
| 6. | Country estimates of areas affected by water erosion | 30 |
| 7. | GLASOD assessment: areas affected by wind erosion | 33 |
| 8. | Country estimates of areas affected by wind erosion | 33 |
| 9. | GLASOD assessment: areas affected by soil fertility decline | 36 |
| 10. | Soil fertility decline: revised estimates | 36 |
| 11. | GLASOD assessment: areas affected by waterlogging | 39 |
| 12A. | Country estimates of areas affected by waterlogging | 40 |
| 12B. | Revised estimates of areas affected by waterlogging | 40 |
| 13. | GLASOD assessment: areas affected by salinization | 42 |
| 14A. | Country estimates of areas affected by salinization | 42 |
| 14B. | Estimates of areas affected by salinization, Pakistan | 42 |
| 14C. | Revised estimates of areas affected by salinization | 44 |
| 15. | GLASOD assessment: areas affected by lowering of the groundwater table | 45 |
| 16. | Estimates of forest are and rate of deforestation | 46 |
| 17. | GLASOD assessment: total areas by degree of degradation | 49 |
| 18. | Best estimates of areas affected by land degradation | 50 |
| 19. | Percentages of agricultural land affected by degradation: summary | 52 |
| 20. | Causes of degradation as given in the GLASOD assessment | 56 |
| 21. | Provisional estimates of the cost of land degradation in the region | 75 |
| 22. | Severity of land degradation in the countries of the region | 90 |

# List of figures

Page

1.  South Asian Region     14
2.  Water erosion severity (GLASOD estimate)     31
3.  Erosion and fertility decline:  GLASOD assessment     32
4.  Wind erosion severity (GLASOD estimate)     34
5.  Pakistan: kilogrammes of wheat produced per kilogramme of nitrogen supplied as fertilizer     37
6.  Waterlogging, salinity and lowering of the water table: GLASOD assessment     40
7.  Salinization severity (GLASOD estimate)     43
8.  Total degradation severity (GLASOD estimate)     48
9.  Causal nexus between land, population, poverty and degradation     62

# Acknowledgements

This study had its origins in collaborative efforts by the countries of South Asia, aware of the increasing problem of land degradation and seeking to assess its magnitude and effects. Work was carried out by means of FAO/UNEP/UNDP Inter-country Project RAS/92/560/A, Study of Land Degradation in South Asia. This report was compiled and written by Anthony Young. Detailed data were contributed by J.S.P. Yadav. The work owes much to advice received from Frank J. Dent, Regional Soil Management and Fertilizer Use Officer, RAPA. Thanks are offered for the kind cooperation of staff of the many institutions visited, including international organizations, regional organizations in Asia, and, in particular, institutions in countries of the region. Additional case study material is contained in a consultant's report by Yadav (1993).

# Summary

## INTRODUCTION

### Origin and objectives

This study originated in Resolution Number 1991/97 of the Economic and Social Council of the United Nations, passed at its 32nd plenary meeting on 26 July 1991, entitled:

> Combating aridity, soil erosion, salinity, waterlogging, desertification and the effects of drought in South Asia.

The Resolution calls for a study to assess the extent of the problem of land degradation and its effects on the peoples of the region, to provide a framework for national and international cooperative efforts to tackle this problem in its physical and human dimensions. The work was carried out by means of a joint FAO/UNEP/UNDP project.

The immediate objective of the project was to undertake a comprehensive study on land degradation in South Asia and its effects upon the people. This specific objectives indicate the aspects covered in this report:

- the status of land degradation: types of degradation, their nature, severity and extent;
- the causes and consequences of land degradation;
- institutions to combat land degradation;
- proposals for strengthening efforts to combat land degradation.

### South Asia region

The **South Asia region**, as covered in this report, comprises eight countries. For purposes of regional comparison they are grouped into two **zones**, with India divided into a dry, western region and a humid region (Figure 1, p. 14):

| Dry zone | Humid zone |
|---|---|
| Afghanistan | Bangladesh |
| India, dry region | Bhutan |
| Iran | India, humid region |
| Pakistan | Nepal |
| | Sri Lanka |

The region has a land area of 641 M ha and a population (1990) of 1200 million. The agricultural population is 768 million, 61% of the total. The area of cropland is 227 M ha, of pasture 94 M ha, and thus of cropland and pasture together, termed *agricultural land*, 321 M ha. These statistics indicate two basic characteristics of the region, which are fundamental to the problems being considered:

□   a high density of population in relation to land resources: over 22% of the world's agricultural population live on just under 5% of its land area;

□   almost all land capable of sustainable agricultural use is already being farmed.


## TYPES OF LAND DEGRADATION

### Definitions

The term **land** refers not just to soil, but to all natural resources which contribute to agricultural production. **Land degradation** is the temporary or permanent lowering of the productive capacity of land. Three **degrees of severity of degradation** are recognized:

Light:         somewhat reduced agricultural productivity;
Moderate:   greatly reduced agricultural productivity;
Strong:       not capable of agricultural production, and unreclaimable at farm level.

**Desertification** is defined by UNEP as land degradation in arid, semi-arid and dry subhumid areas resulting from adverse human impact. In this report, therefore, it is equivalent to land degradation in the dry zone.

### Types of land degradation

The following types of land degradation are assessed:

-   water erosion;
-   wind erosion;
-   soil fertility decline;
-   waterlogging;
-   salinization;
-   lowering of the water table.

Three other types are considered in more generalized terms:

-   deforestation (covered by reference to FAO data);
-   forest degradation;
-   rangeland degradation.

Soil pollution, urban encroachment onto agricultural land, and the potential effects of global climatic change, whilst well recognized as actual or potential problems, have not been assessed in this study.

### Reversible degradation and land reclamation

The effects of water and wind erosion are largely irreversible. Although plant nutrients and soil organic matter may be restored, to replace the actual loss of soil material would require taking the soil out of use for many thousand of years, an impractical course of action.

In other cases, land degradation is reversible: soils with reduced organic matter can be restored by additions of plant residues, degraded pastures may recover under improved range management. Salinized soils can be restored to productive use, although at a high cost, through salinity control and reclamation projects.

The cost of reclamation, or restoration to productive use, of degraded soils is normally much higher than the cost of preventing degradation before it has occurred.

## SOURCE OF DATA

The major source of data employed is the *Global assessment of soil degradation* (GLASOD). Other sources are material assembled by the Asian Problem Soils Network, and estimates by individual countries. The GLASOD estimates are taken as the primary basis for this report, modified where the balance of evidence suggested a need to do so. For deforestation, data are taken from the FAO *Forest resources assessment 1990 project*.

The available data on the extent and severity of degradation are highly variable. Reasons are first, a failure to define in sufficiently precise terms what is meant by the various degrees of severity of degradation; and secondly, the absence of reliable surveys over large areas.

## STATUS OF LAND DEGRADATION

Best estimates from an assessment of the status of land degradation are given in detail in Table 18 (p. 50). Combining the degrees of severity, and giving totals for the dry zone, the humid zone, and the South Asian region, summary data are shown in Table 19 (p. 52).

**Water erosion** is the most widespread form of degradation, affecting some 25% of agricultural land. It is found widely in both the dry and humid zones. In many areas of sloping land, for example in Nepal, it has reached severe proportions, causing or threatening the permanent loss of the productive capacity of land.

**Wind erosion** is estimated to affect of the order of 40% of agricultural land in the dry zone, although quantitative evidence for definition of its degrees of severity is lacking.

**Soil fertility decline**, formerly not as widely recognized as other types of degradation, is a substantial and widespread problem in the region. It occurs through a combination of lowering of soil organic matter and loss of nutrients. Evidence for fertility decline includes data on:

- soil organic matter depletion;
- a negative soil nutrient balance;
- imbalance in fertilizer application;
- secondary and micronutrient deficiencies;
- failure of increases in fertilizer use to be matched by increase in crop yield;
- lower responses to fertilizers.

**Waterlogging** affects some irrigated lands on the alluvial plains and interior basins. Whilst less extensive than other types of degradation on a regional scale, it is severe in some areas.

**Salinization** (including sodification) is a severe problem on irrigated lands of the dry zone. It is found both in light to moderate degrees, reducing crop yield, and in the severe degree, causing complete abandonment of formerly productive irrigated land. Salinization through intrusion of salt water is also found in coastal areas.

**Lowering of the groundwater table** has occurred in certain irrigated areas where the groundwater remains non-saline.

Although waterlogging, salinization and lowering of the water table are of smaller extent than other types of degradation, their consequences are proportionally greater, since they mainly affect irrigated lands which are potentially the most productive.

A summary of the severity of land degradation with respect to the countries of the region, including the above six types together with **deforestation** and **rangeland degradation** is given in Table 22 (p. 90).

The countries of the dry zone – Afghanistan, Iran, Pakistan and the western part of India – are severely affected by water and wind erosion, soil fertility decline, deforestation and rangeland degradation. Their alluvial plain and basin areas are affected by waterlogging, salinization and lowering of the water table. By definition, therefore, these countries are severely affected by desertification.

Four countries of the humid zone – Bangladesh, Nepal, Sri Lanka and the greater part of India – are severely affected by water erosion on their rainfed lands, by soil fertility decline, and by deforestation. In parts of the hill and mountain areas of Nepal, deforestation and water erosion have reached an extreme degree. Bhutan, because of its lower population density, has not yet suffered severe land degradation, but deforestation, often the first set leading towards degradation, is taking place.

The problem of **soil fertility decline** has not previously received sufficient attention. On a national scale, increases in crop yields are falling behind rates of increase in fertilizer use. Surveys have shown that soil organic matter levels are falling. Micronutrient deficiencies are being widely reported, where farmers have attempted to sustain yields by application of major nutrients only. In long-term experiments, yield responses are declining except where fertilizer is applied in conjunction with organic manure. This form of degradation is found in both the humid and dry zones. Whilst its widespread occurrence is not in doubt, quantitative estimates of its extent and severity will require further surveys and monitoring of soil changes.

## CAUSES OF DEGRADATION

### Natural degradation hazards, direct causes and underlying causes

Land degradation results from cultural degradation hazards, direct causes, and underlying causes.

**Natural degradation hazards** are conditions of the natural environment which lead to high susceptibility to degradation, for example steep slopes, rains of high intensity, strong leaching in humid regions, and drought in dry regions.

**Direct causes of degradation** are unsuitable land use and inappropriate land management practices. These vary with the type of degradation. They include:

- deforestation of fragile land, unsuitable for sustained agricultural use;
- overcutting of vegetation (which is very widespread);
- shifting cultivation without adequate fallow periods;
- overgrazing;
- non-adoption of soil conservation management practices;
- extension of cultivation onto lands of low potential or high natural hazards;
- improper crop rotations;
- plant nutrient deficits in soils, with negative budgets over many years;
- unbalanced fertilizer use;
- problems arising from planning and management of irrigation systems;
- overpumping of groundwater, in excess of capacity for recharge.

**Underlying causes of degradation** are the basic reasons which give rise to the direct causes. These are:

- land shortage;
- land tenure: short-term or insecure tenancy, open access resources;
- economic pressures;
- poverty;
- population increase.

### The causal nexus between land, population and degradation

The direct and indirect causes of land degradation are linked by a causal nexus (Figure 9, p. 62). The two external, or driving, forces are *limited land resources* and *increase in rural population*. These combine to produce *land shortage*, resulting in small farms, low production per person and increasing landlessness. A consequence of land shortage is *poverty*.

Land shortage and poverty, taken together, lead to *non-sustainable land management practices*, the direct causes of degradation. This has the effect of increasing land shortage, a vicious cycle of cause and effect. "It is population growth working in conjunction with other factors that is bringing about widespread environmental deterioration" (FAO/RAPA, 1990, p. 10) "...environmental degradation perpetuates poverty, as the poorest groups attempt to survive on a diminishing resource base" (FAO, 1992, p. 106).

There are two ways to intervene in this nexus: improved technology and reduction of population increase. Increased efforts should certainly be made in research into improved technologies especially their more widespread implementation. However, it must be emphasized that **all efforts at improved technology will be nullified and in places reversed unless they are accompanied by a reduction in the rate of growth of population.** A much greater integration between population policy, agriculture, and land resource management is needed.

For this to occur, new attitudes are required. There is growing recognition of the need to link population policy with development. "Population issues currently encompass areas of concern such as poverty alleviation, environmental degradation ... which are much broader than population size and growth alone" (ESCAP, 1991, para. 529). "Few institutions have developed a response strategy to the implications of population pressure on natural resource management (Asian Development Bank, 1991, p. 21). "The close link between poverty and environmental problems make a compelling case of increasing assistance to reduce poverty and slow population growth" (World Bank, 1992). A much grater integration between population policy and agriculture and land resource management is needed.

## ECONOMIC CONSEQUENCES OF DEGRADATION

### The economic cost of degradation

An attempt has been made to estimate the economic cost of land degradation. Many of the critical assumptions are based on tentative data, particularly the relative production loss resulting from different degrees of degradation. The results are therefore provisional, and refer to orders of magnitude of the macroeconomic effects.

The estimates are based primarily on the measurement of two variables: production loss and replacement cost. Production loss is the reduced productivity of the soil as a consequence of degradation, expressed as a percentage of production from the undegraded soil. For erosion and soil fertility decline, the assumptions are a 5-10% production loss for a light degree of degradation, 20% for moderate and 75% for strong degradation, for the case of salinity, the respective losses assumed, based on experimental data, are 15, 65 and 100% respectively. Replacement cost is the cost of additional inputs (primarily fertilizer) used by farmers in order to maintain production levels on the degraded soils. Price assumptions are US$200 per tonne for cereals and US$300 per tonne of fertilizer nutrients.

Summing the estimates for the direct on-site costs of land degradation shown in Table 21 (p. 75) gives a total of US$9.8 - US$11.0 thousand million per year. Thus, in round figures, the cumulative effect of human-induced land degradation is estimated to cost countries of the region a sum on the order of US$ 10 thousand million per year. Addition of the off-site effects of erosion would substantially increase this figure.

The on-site cost is equivalent to 2% of the gross domestic product of the region, or 7% of its agricultural gross domestic product. The inclusion of off-site effects of water erosion would substantially increases this value.

### Discussion

A 'contrary' view exists, which states:

> "Estimates of the extent of land degradation, or of their effects on production, may
> be considerably exaggerated. Unless and until there is a better foundation of
> evidence, the problem does not meet the criteria for development investment."

This view serves one important purpose, in that it places emphasis on what are, indeed, large uncertainties in estimates of the extent of degradation and its effects.

Although some of the estimates are based on questionable foundations, reports from all countries of the region point to the certain existence of two kinds of situation:

- Severe degradation over substantial, identifiable, areas; e.g. gullying, total removal of topsoil by sheet erosion, complete salinization.
- Light to moderate degradation over extensive areas; e.g. soil fertility decline and desertification of rangelands.

**It is therefore concluded that, although more precise data should be obtained, the total evidence is sufficient to call for immediate action to prevent further land degradation and, where possible, to reverse the effects of past degradation.**

## EFFECTS UPON THE PEOPLE

The effects of land degradation may be grouped as effects upon production and consequences for the people.

The **effects upon production** are:

- abandonment of land, where degradation has reached a severe degree;
- reduced crop yields;
- increased inputs and greater costs where farmers, out of necessity, attempt to combat reduction in yields with increased inputs, primarily of fertilizers;
- reduced responses to inputs;
- reduced productivity of irrigated land, thereby leading to less efficient use of the high inputs which have gone into development of irrigation;
- lower flexibility of land management;
- greater risk;
- loss of water for irrigation;
- diversion of labour, technical and financial resources to reclamation.

The **consequences for the people** are:

- increased landlessness;
- reduced and less reliable food supplies;
- increased labour requirements;
- lower incomes.

Land degradation has its most serious effects upon the poor. Poor farmers, primarily those with small landholdings, have neither the resources to combat land degradation nor the options to meet short-term disasters, such as flood, drought, attack by pests, or war. It is the poor who, by force of circumstances, suffer most from the nexus of land, population, poverty and degradation.

## INSTITUTIONS AND PROGRAMMES TO COMBAT DEGRADATION

### National institutions

Institutional structures to combat land degradation may be grouped into institutions responsible for strategy and policy, research, and implementation.

Bangladesh, India, and Pakistan possess large and complex institutional structures for these purposes. Other countries in the region have structures which are smaller but still (with the exception of Bhutan) moderately complex. The operation of institutions in Afghanistan is seriously hindered by current political conditions.

Whilst most institutional questions are specific to countries, two features are commonly found:

- there is tendency towards unduly complex structures, with overlapping responsibilities;
- research and planning are often more advanced than implementation in the field.

The subject of land resources should become recognized as a major division of environmental affairs. **Land resources** cover the sustainable use of the resources of climate, water, soils, landform and vegetation, combining productive use with conservation. Countries should seek to clarify institutional responsibilities in the area of land resources.

## Environmental legislation

It is recognized that improvements in environmental legislation have a role to play in combating land degradation. It has not been possible, however, to include a review of such legislation in this study.

## Regional collaborative programmes

The fight against land degradation has received support from regional collaborative programmes, in particular:

- Asian network on problem soils.
- Desertification control in Asia and the Pacific (DESCONAP).
- Fertilizer and development network for Asia and the Pacific (FADINAP).
- Forestry research support programme for Asia and the Pacific (FORSPA).
- Asian bio and organic fertilizer network.

These networks continue to play an important role in exchange of ideas and formulation of policy and programmes.

## PROPOSALS FOR ACTION

### Introduction

If integrated action is not taken to combat both the direct and the indirect causes of land degradation:

- resources will be destroyed, in some cases irreversibly;
- there will be further considerable economic losses at the national level;
- the people, and in particular the poor, will suffer.

A prerequisite for effective action is recognition, by national governments, of the severity of land degradation and its effects upon people. It is not sufficient to pay lip service to 'environment' nor to write reports. There must be allocation of staff, budget and resources.

**Proposals for action**

Seven proposals are made, for action to strengthen efforts to combat land degradation. They are confined to the main lines of approach and action. Many of the proposed actions will initially require discussion on a regional, and in some cases global, basis, in order to secure uniformity of methods. They will subsequently require modifications in detail to meet the circumstances of different countries.

1.  **Practical definitions of degrees of severity of land degradation.** These must be in terms that offer practical means of observation, monitoring and mapping. This action is best taken at international level, in order to achieve comparability of information worldwide.

2.  **Establishment of a regional programme and guidelines for the assessment of land degradation.** This should include:

    -   **survey** of the present state of degradation;
    -   **monitoring** of soil changes.

3.  **Study of the economic and social effects upon the people**. Ideally, such work should be conducted in parallel with physical surveys, with cooperation in the field between land resources scientists and social scientists.

4.  **Translation of these guidelines into national programmes.** Aspects to be covered are:

    -   **Clarify institutional responsibilities**. It may be necessary to establish high-level advisory committees on land degradation policy.
    -   Identify **nodal institutions** for land degradation.
    -   **Identify priorities**, with respect to types of degradation and critical areas.
    -   Plan and carry out **national programmes.**

5.  **Research into measures to combat degradation.** Practical field implementation needs to be continuously supported by research. Particular attention should be given to research into:

    -   practical methods of improving and maintaining soil organic matter status;
    -   ways of securing participation of the people in the implementation of improved measures of land management, for example soil conservation measures which provide intrinsic incentives for the land users;
    -   research into the underlying causes of degradation, and the integration of land resources management with wider aspects of population policy.

6.  **Implementation of measures to combat the direct causes of degradation.** Much activity of this nature is already being undertaken, but the scale of activity needs to be expanded. Increased funding will be required. Measures of this type include:

    -   watershed management and soil conservation projects and extension work;

- method for improving soil organic matter status;
- application of integrated plant nutrition systems;
- salinity control and reclamation projects;
- reafforestation;
- further development of agroforestry, including for soil conservation;
- control of desertification, including sand dune fixation, and improved rangeland management.

**7.  Action directed towards removing the underlying causes of degradation, including integration of land management measures with population policy.**

Attempts to combat land degradation directly, by conservation measures or land reclamation, can have only short-term effects unless they are accompanied by efforts to tackle the underlying causes. These lie in the causal nexus between population increase, limited land resources, land shortage, poverty, non-sustainable land management practices, and land degradation. In the prevailing situation in which there is no spare land available, population increases of 2-3% per year will largely or entirely counteract the effects of measures for improvement.

Population is a sensitive issue, but all governments of the region are aware of the problems caused by continued increase at present rates. In the context of land degradation, a much greater integration between population policy, agriculture and land resource management is needed. For this to occur, new attitudes will be required.

# Chapter 1

# Introduction

**Origin, objectives and constraints**

*Origin of the study*

This study originated in Resolution Number 1991/97 of the Economic and Social Council of the United Nations, passed at its 32nd plenary meeting on 26th July 1991, entitled:

> Combating aridity, soil erosion, salinity, water-logging, desertification and the effects of drought in South Asia.

This begins by recalling a General Assembly resolution of 1989 which stressed the imperative need to address the problem of desertification. It notes that South Asia is one of the most populous regions of the world, and that it contains significant areas subject to soil erosion, salinity and other kind of degradation, "which affect the lives of millions of peoples and the entire environment of the region".

The Resolution then:

> "Requests the Secretary-General, in close collaboration with the Executive Director of the United Nations Environment Programme... [and other organizations]...to undertake a study...to assess the extent of this problem and its effects on the peoples of the region, and to provide a framework for national and international cooperative efforts...to tackle this problem in its physical and human dimensions, and to submit the study to the Economic and Social Council in 1992."

Consultations were held between UNEP, UNDP, FAO and ESCAP[1], leading to the preparation of draft outline and work plan for the study. This latter made clear that the focus was to be on the problem of land degradation, and the human impacts on natural resources which reduce their productive capacity.

FAO was selected as the Executing Agency. A Project Document was drawn up as Project Number RAS/92/560/A/01/12, with a duration of four months, entitled *Study of land degradation in South Asia*. This defines South Asia for the purpose of the study as including eight countries of the ESCAP region: Afghanistan, Bangladesh, Bhutan, India, Iran, Nepal, Pakistan, and Sri Lanka. Data was to be made available from sources of UNDP, UNEP, FAO, ESCAP, the World Bank, UNCED, and by means of limited visits to selected countries of the region. The project document further sets out the outputs and objectives.

---

[1]    Economic and Social Council for Asia and the Pacific.

## *Objectives*

The immediate objective of the project is **to undertake a comprehensive study on combating aridity, soil erosion, salinity, waterlogging, desertification and the effects of drought in South Asia**, for submission to the Secretary General of the United Nations in response to ECOSOC Resolution 1991/97.

The contents specified for the report constitute the objectives of the study. These are to review, analyse and summarize:

1.  The status of land degradation in South Asia.
2.  The causes of land degradation, and its effects on the people of the region.
3.  Existing institutions and current national and international cooperative programmes to combat land degradation.
4.  To suggest a framework for strengthening national and international cooperative efforts to tackle land degradation in its physical and human dimensions, at national, regional and international levels.

In carrying out the study, an attempt has been made to give equal attention to the first two of these objectives: the status, meaning the nature, extent and severity, of land degradation; and its effects, social and economic, upon the people.

## *Constraints*

The range of material to be covered is vast and the time available short, less than six person-months. It was therefore necessary to base the study entirely on existing publications and reports, supplemented by discussions with staff members of national and international institutions.

Over 200 publications and reports based on the region were consulted. Two were of fundamental importance. Extensive use was made of a recent comprehensive and primary study, the *Global assessment of land degradation (GLASOD)* (Oldeman *et al.*, 1990; UNEP, 1992a). Besides the published maps and data, the organizations responsible, UNEP and ISRIC, made available primary data for the region. The second starting point was the report of the FAO/RAPA consultation, *Environmental issues in land and water development* (FAO/RAPA, 1992). This includes a regional review (Dent, 1992) and country papers on Bangladesh, India, Nepal, Pakistan and Sri Lanka.

The study was based on the FAO Regional Office for Asia and the Pacific (RAPA), Bangkok. Time shortage and political conditions placed constraints on field visits. Short visits were made to five countries of the region: Bangladesh, India, Nepal, Pakistan and Sri Lanka, to conduct interviews with staff of organizations engaged in research into land degradation and efforts to combat its effects. Discussions were also held with staff of the World Bank and the World Resources Institute, Washington DC. Publications were consulted in the FAO Library, Rome, and the FAO and United Nations Libraries, Bangkok.

It should be emphasized that the time and human resources available to carry out this study were extremely limited in comparison with the magnitude of the task to be carried out. Consequently, the results should be regarded as provisional and subject to modification. A call for further and more detailed studies is made in the recommendations.

## Background to the South Asia region

### Land and population

Eight countries are included in the region (Figure 1):

| Short title | Full title |
|---|---|
| Afghanistan | Democratic Republic of Afghanistan |
| Bangladesh | People's Republic of Bangladesh |
| Bhutan | Kingdom of Bhutan |
| India | Republic of India |
| Iran | Islamic Republic of Iran |
| Nepal | Kingdom of Nepal |
| Pakistan | Islamic Republic of Pakistan |
| Sri Lanka | Democratic Socialist Republic of Sri Lanka |

Throughout this study, these eight countries are called *the South Asian region* or, in short, *the region*.

The region has a land area of 641 M ha and a population (1990) of 1200 million (Tables 1 and 2). The agricultural population is 768 million, 61% of the total. The area of cropland is 227 M ha, of pasture 94 M ha, and thus of cropland and pasture together, here called *agricultural land*, 321 M ha.

These bare statistics indicate three basic characteristics of the region: the large total population, high density in relation to land resources, and large proportion of total land under agricultural use. Over 22% of the world's agricultural population live on just under 5% of its land area; whilst almost exactly 50% of the total land is under agricultural use, a far higher proportion than for the world as a whole.

India has 46% of the land area of the region but 71% of its population. Iran is the next largest country in terms of area, but Pakistan and Bangladesh have the second and third largest populations.

These high agricultural population densities result in low availability of land. On average, there are 0.31 ha of cropland per capita, 0.13 ha of pasture, or a total of 0.44 ha of agricultural land per capita. With the possible exception of Bhutan, for which data are uncertain, Bangladesh has the highest agricultural population density, with 0.12 ha of agricultural land per capita.

The problems which arise from this situation are becoming more severe through population increase, which for the region as a whole averages 2.39% per year. The 1990 population of 1200 million will have become some 1265 million by 1993. Despite a growth of urbanization in relative terms, the agricultural population is increasing at some 1.7% per year.

Little or no expansion of cropland is taking place, and opportunities for expansion of the irrigated area are limited. Thus, the area of cropland will have fallen from 0.31 to about 0.29 ha per capita agricultural population in the three years 1990-1993.

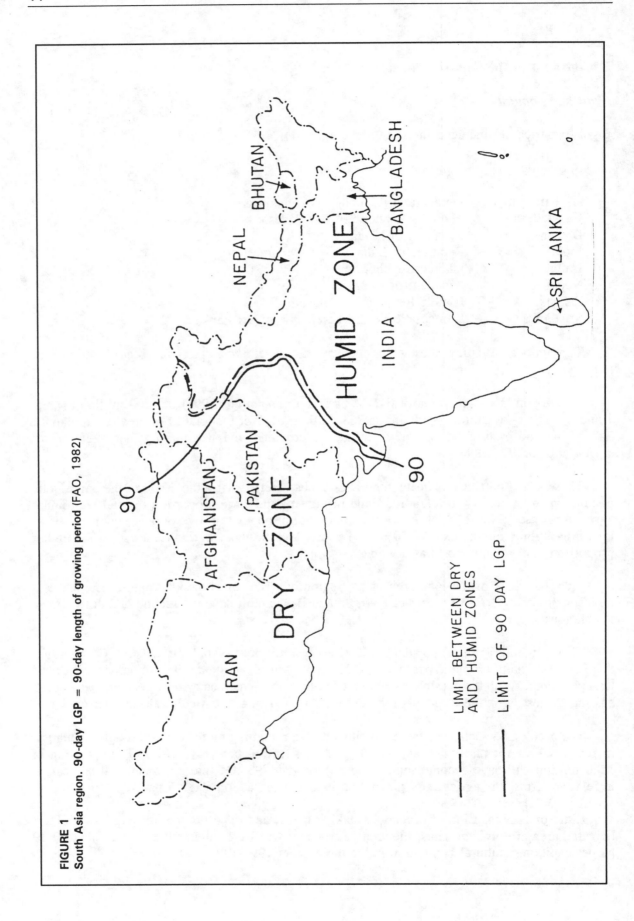

**FIGURE 1**
South Asia region. 90-day LGP = 90-day length of growing period (FAO, 1982)

TABLE 1
**Land use in South Asia, 1990**

| Country | Total Land | Arable and permanent crops | | Permanent pasture | | Forests and woodlands | | Other land | |
|---|---|---|---|---|---|---|---|---|---|
| | (Mha) | (Mha) | % | (Mha) | % | (Mha) | % | (Mha) | % |
| Afghanistan* | 65.21 | 8.05 | 12 | 30.00 | 46 | 1.90 | 3 | 25.26 | 39 |
| Bangladesh | 13.02 | 9.13 | 70 | 0.60 | 5 | 1.86 | 14 | 1.42 | 11 |
| Bhutan | 4.70 | 0.13 | 3 | 0.27 | 6 | 2.61 | 56 | 1.69 | 35 |
| India | 297.32 | 169.08 | 57 | 12.05 | 4 | 66.70 | 22 | 49.49 | 17 |
| Iran | 163.60 | 15.05 | 9 | 44.00 | 27 | 18.02 | 11 | 86.53 | 53 |
| Nepal | 13.68 | 2.65 | 19 | 2.00 | 15 | 2.48 | 18 | 6.55 | 48 |
| Pakistan | 77.09 | 20.75 | 27 | 5.00 | 6 | 3.55 | 5 | 47.79 | 62 |
| Sri Lanka | 6.46 | 1.90 | 29 | 0.44 | 7 | 2.08 | 32 | 2.04 | 32 |
| Region | 641.08 | 226.74 | 35 | 94.36 | 15 | 99.20 | 15 | 220.78 | 35 |
| Asia-Pacific | 3 001.46 | 453.32 | 15 | 1 036.83 | 23 | 660.20 | 22 | 851.12 | 28 |
| World | 13 079.15 | 1 444.22 | 11 | 3 402.08 | 26 | 4 027.57 | 31 | 4 205.29 | 32 |

Source:    RAPA (1992).

*    FAO Production Yearbook, Vol. 45, 1991.

TABLE 2
**Land and population in South Asia, 1990**

| Country | Total land area | Total population | Population density | Population growth rate (1980-90) | Agricultural population | Land per capita | | |
|---|---|---|---|---|---|---|---|---|
| | | | | | | Agricultural land[1] | Cropland[2] | Permanent pasture |
| | (Mha) | (million) | (per Km²) | (% per year) | (million) | (ha) | (ha) | (ha) |
| Afghanistan | 65.21 | 16.56 | 30 | 2.6 | 9.07 | 4.20 | 0.89 | 3.31 |
| Bangladesh | 13.02 | 115.59 | 888 | 2.3 | 79.22 | 0.12 | 0.12 | 0.01 |
| Bhutan | 4.70 | 1.52 | 32 | 2.1 | 1.38 | 0.29 | 0.10 | 0.20 |
| India | 297.32 | 853.09 | 287 | 2.1 | 535.60 | 0.34 | 0.32 | 0.02 |
| Iran | 163.60 | 54.61 | 33 | 3.6 | 14.64 | 4.03 | 1.03 | 3.01 |
| Nepal | 13.68 | 19.14 | 139 | 2.6 | 17.56 | 0.26 | 0.15 | 0.11 |
| Pakistan | 77.09 | 122.63 | 159 | 3.1 | 64.94 | 0.40 | 0.32 | 0.08 |
| Sri Lanka | 6.46 | 17.22 | 267 | 1.4 | 8.90 | 0.26 | 0.21 | 0.05 |
| Region | 641.08 | 1 200.36 | 187 | 2.39 | 731.31 | 0.44 | 0.31 | 0.13 |
| Asia-Pacific | 3 001.46 | 2 980.23 | 99 | 1.84 | 1 738.81 | 0.86 | 0.26 | 0.60 |
| World | 13 079.15 | 5 314.75 | 41 | 1.75 | 2 389.91 | 2.03 | 0.60 | 1.42 |

Source:    RAPA (1992); FAO Production Yearbook, Vol. 45, 1991.

[1]    Agricultural land = Cropland plus permanent pasture.
[2]    Cropland = Arable and permanent crops.

Results from the FAO study of population supporting capacities serve to emphasize the special position of the region (FAO, 1982). Even in 1975, the actual populations exceeded the capacity of land to support them at a low level of inputs for six of the eight countries, whilst Pakistan was close to this limit. Afghanistan, Bangladesh and Iran were close to the limits for population supporting capacity at an intermediate input level, and were projected to exceed these at their estimated population levels in the year 2000.

This is the basic situation in the region: a large and growing population pressing upon an area of land which offers little opportunity for further expansion. As will be shown, the problems which arise from this position are now being aggravated by a decline in the land resource base through degradation.

## *Environment*

A brief summary of some major features of the physical environment of the region serves two purposes. First, it indicates some climatic, landform and soil features which give rise to natural hazards of degradation, such as steep slopes and rainfall of high intensity. Secondly, it is the basis for the major contrasts in the types of land degradation found in different parts of the region.

Only an outline is given. Further details will be found in reports of the agro-ecological zones study (FAO, 1978-80), and in publications for individual countries listed in the references. Additional sources are given in an annotated bibliography, *1993 Directory of Country Environmental Studies* (World Resources Institute, 1992).

**Climate**  Four of the eight countries - Bangladesh, Bhutan, Nepal and Sri Lanka - have predominantly humid climates, whilst three, Afghanistan, Pakistan and Iran, have predominantly dry climates. India lies across this major climatic divide, humid or subhumid over some 75% of its area, semi-arid to arid in the north-western quarter. The line of the 90-day growing period serves to demarcate the boundary between these two zones (FAO, 1982).

This broad climatic grouping is here used as the basis for summarizing land degradation on a regional scale. India is divided into "India, dry region" and "India, humid region", separated by the line marking a 90-day growing period. Two climatic zones are employed (Figure 1):

| Dry zone[1] | Humid zone |
|---|---|
| Afghanistan | Bangladesh |
| India, dry region | Bhutan |
| Iran | India, humid region |
| Pakistan | Nepal |
| | Sri Lanka |

---

[1]   Because of the difficulty of separating data, the whole of Afghanistan and Pakistan are included in the Dry Zone, even though these countries include areas with more than 90 days length of growing period.

Two climatic features lead to high natural hazards of degradation. First, the rainfall of the humid zone is monsoonal in character, falling in limited periods of the year and often with high intensity, giving a high liability to water erosion. Secondly, rainfall in the dry zone is not only low but highly variable, leading to recurrent droughts and the consequences for wind erosion and desertification.

**Landform**  Major contrasts in the status of land degradation also originate from the three major physiographic regions which occupy the region:

□ The mountain belt of the Himalayas, Hindu Kush and associated mountain area of Iran. This belt stretches along the whole northern border of the region, including parts of all countries except Sri Lanka.

□ The alluvial plains of the Indus and Ganges river systems of India and Pakistan, with which may be grouped the interior basins of Iran.

□ The uplands of the Deccan of India, together with the central hill massif of Sri Lanka.

The nature of the river systems in the northern part of the region is of special significance. These originate in the snows and high rainfall areas of the mountain belt, from which they flow across the alluvial plains. This offers a major resource for agriculture, but at the same time, presents specific problems of water management.

The steep slopes of the mountain belt lead to high hazard of soil erosion by water, whilst in association with the monsoonal rainfall, this hazard is also considerable in the uplands. The alluvial plains give rise to special problems associated with management of their rivers and groundwater resources.

**Soils**  Because of the range of climatic, geological and physiographic conditions, virtually all of the major soil types of tropical areas occur in the region, together with some characteristic of subtropical and mountain zones. Strongly leached ferralsols and acrisols are widespread in the humid zone, whilst the volcanic lavas of the western Deccan carry an extensive area of vertisols (black, cracking clays). In the more humid parts of the alluvial plains, cambisols and fluvisols (alluvial soils) are extensive. The dry zone includes large areas of calcisols and fluvisols, and in Iran, naturally occurring solonchaks (saline soils).

Of special relevance is the large extent of what have been termed *problem soils*, those which present special problems for agricultural use. In a recent review, eleven types of problems soils were identified, with a combined extent of over 80% of the land area of the region (Dent, 1990). Areas of problem soils are also called 'fragile lands', meaning that they have a high degradation hazard if not carefully managed. Parts of them have also been called 'marginal lands', meaning that they lie close to the margin for sustainable agricultural use.

Each type of problem soil leads to specific hazards for degradation. In terms of area covered, the most widespread problems are steeply sloping land, dry land, and land with severe fertility limitations (Dent, 1990, p.67).

**Vegetation**  A high proportion of the humid zone was once covered with forest, but because of the long period of habitation by the ancient civilizations of the region, large areas of this would already have been cleared at least a thousand years ago. The forest which remains is concentrated in the mountain and hill areas, where it constitutes a major natural resource, protecting the slopes from erosion and stabilizing the flow of rivers. Deforestation of these areas is now widespread, being at the same time a form of land degradation in itself and a cause of other types of degradation.

The dry zone is occupied by various types of open woodland and grassland. Because of the limited opportunities for cultivation, these vegetation formations constitute a major resource for land use in the zone. As discussed below, this resource has been greatly reduced by degradation, both of the woody and herbaceous components of the vegetation.

*Irrigation systems*

Although not forming part of the natural environment, irrigation systems have been widely developed in the region, such that they now make a major contribution to its land resources. Four types of systems may be distinguished, each presenting different problems of management and hazards of degradation:

1.  The large reservoir-and-canal based systems of the alluvial plains of the Indus and Ganges.
2.  Areas of groundwater irrigation on these same plains, originally from shallow hand-constructed wells, now mainly from power-driven tubewells.
3.  The varied systems of the Deccan uplands and Sri Lanka, including those based on major reservoirs, small earth dams ('tanks'), and wells. In Sri Lanka, some of these systems are of ancient origin, now rehabilitated.
4.  The complex systems found in Iran and Afghanistan, including the ancient method using underground channels ('qanats').

Management of the surface and groundwater resources of these irrigation systems has led to extensive problems, particularly waterlogging and salinization.

**Arrangement of the report**

Following this introduction, the Report can be grouped into four parts, corresponding to the objectives of the study.

**Objective 1:**

**The status of land degradation:**                                                      **Chapters 2-5**

**Objective 2:**

**The causes and consequences of land degradation**                                      **Chapters 6-8**

**Objective 3:**

**Institutions to combat degradation**                                                   **Chapter 9**

**Objective 4:**

**Conclusions, and proposals for strengthening efforts to combat
land degradation**                                                                       **Chapter 10**

Chapter 2

# Types of land degradation

## DEFINITIONS

The term land, as employed in land evaluation, land use planning, etc., has a wider meaning than just soil. It refers to all natural resources which contribute to agricultural production, including livestock production and forestry. Land thus covers climate and water resources, landform, soils and vegetation, including both grassland resources and forests (FAO, 1976; UNEP, 1992b).

**Land degradation** is the temporary or permanent lowering of the productive capacity of land (UNEP, 1992b). It thus covers the various forms of soil degradation, adverse human impacts on water resources, deforestation, and lowering of the productive capacity of rangelands.

This study takes the degradation of soil resources as its focus. This includes soil erosion by water and wind, deterioration in soil physical, chemical and biological properties, waterlogging, and the build-up of toxicities, particularly salts, in the soil. Since soil productivity is intimately connected with water availability, lowering of the groundwater table is also noted. Since deforestation is being treated in detail in a current FAO study, it is here considered primarily as a cause of soil degradation, particularly erosion.

Land degradation has both on-site and off-site effects. **On-site effects** are the lowering of the productive capacity of the land, causing either reduced outputs (crop yields, livestock yields) or the need for increased inputs. **Off-site effects** of water erosion occur through changes in the water regime, including decline in river water quality, and sedimentation of river beds and reservoirs. The main off-site effect of wind erosion is overblowing, or sand deposition.

**Desertification** The term desertification originated with a specific meaning, as for example in the 1977 *World map of desertification* (UNEP, 1977). It was subsequently widely used and misused in a broader sense. These wider meanings have sometimes been extended to almost all forms of land degradation, for example soil erosion in the humid tropics (Young, 1985). The recent *World atlas of desertification* (UNEP, 1992a) includes all the six groups of land degradation covered in the present study thus implicitly, from its title, using the term in the broader sense.

Following agreement at a recent UNEP conference, the term has been defined with a more restricted meaning:

**Desertification** is land degradation in arid, semi-arid and dry subhumid areas resulting from adverse human impact (UNEP, 1992b).

This is the meaning in which the term is employed in the ESCAP network on desertification (ESCAP, 1983, 1991b). In this study, therefore, desertification is equivalent to land degradation in the dry zone, and need not be separately assessed as a type of degradation.

## TYPES OF LAND DEGRADATION ASSESSED

For the purpose of this study, the many and varied processes of land degradation have been grouped into six classes: water erosion, wind erosion, soil fertility decline, salinization, waterlogging, and lowering of the water table.

**Water erosion** covers all forms of soil erosion by water, including sheet and rill erosion and gullying. Human-induced intensification of landsliding, caused by vegetation clearance, road construction, etc., is also included.

**Wind erosion** refers to loss of soil by wind, occurring primarily in dry regions.

**Soil fertility decline** is used as a short term to refer to what is more precisely described as deterioration in soil physical, chemical and biological properties. Whilst decline in fertility is indeed a major effect of erosion, the term is used here of cover effects of processes other than erosion. The main processes involved are:

□   lowering of soil organic matter, with associated decline in soil biological activity;
□   degradation of soil physical properties (structure, aeration, water holding capacity), as brought about by reduced organic matter;
□   adverse changes in soil nutrient resources, including reduction in availability of the major nutrients (nitrogen, phosphorus, potassium), onset of micronutrient deficiencies, and development of nutrient imbalances.
□   buildup of toxicities, primarily acidification through incorrect fertilizer use.

**Waterlogging** is the lowering in land productivity through the rise in groundwater close to the soil surface. Also included under this heading is the severe form, termed ponding, where the water table rises above the surface. Waterlogging is linked with salinization, both being brought about by incorrect irrigation management.

**Salinization** is used in its broad sense, to refer to all types of soil degradation brought about by the increase of salts in the soil. It thus covers both salinization in its strict sense, the buildup of free salts; and sodification (also called alkalization), the development of dominance of the exchange complex by sodium. As human-induced processes, these occur mainly through incorrect planning and management of irrigation schemes. Also covered is saline intrusion, the incursion of sea water into coastal soils arising from over-abstraction of groundwater.

**Lowering of the water table** is a self-explanatory form of land degradation, brought about through tubewell pumping of groundwater for irrigation exceeding the natural recharge capacity. This occurs in areas of non-saline ('sweet') groundwater. Pumping for urban and industrial use is a further cause.

## OTHER TYPES OF DEGRADATION INCLUDED

Other types of land degradation are treated briefly, treated as causes, or excluded from this review. This is because they are localized or of small extent on a regional scale, or because they are more fully treated elsewhere.

Four further classes are recognized as types of land degradation, and as having considerable importance in the region. One case, deforestation, has been treated by reference to an external review. The two other types are considered in more generalized terms.

**Deforestation** The occurrence of deforestation is widespread and extremely serious in the region. It is not independently assessed here, in view of more detailed treatment in the current FAO *Forest resources assessment 1990 project*. Deforestation is also discussed as a cause of erosion.

**Forest degradation** This is the reduction of biotic resources and lowering of productive capacity of forests through human activities. It is under review in a current survey (Banerjee and Grimes, in preparation).

**Rangeland degradation** This is the lowering of the productive capacity of rangelands. It is considered in generalized terms, but no quantitative data have been identified.

## TYPES OF DEGRADATION EXCLUDED FROM THE STUDY

Other types of degradation are excluded from this study, either because they are of small extent on a regional scale, or they are more fully treated elsewhere. These are:

- **Acid sulphate formation**, a serious but localized form of degradation, which may occur on drainage of coastal swamps.

- **Soil pollution**, from industrial or mining effluents, to the atmosphere, rivers or groundwater. This is an important concern in the region, but is strongly localized.

- **Soil destruction through mining and quarrying activities**, the failure to restore soil after extraction. The same remarks apply as for soil pollution.

- **Urban and industrial encroachment onto agricultural land.** With the projected increase in urbanization, this will continue to be a substantial cause of loss of agricultural land, but it is a different problem from land degradation.

- **Effects of war.** Land degradation on a substantial scale through effects of war has been reported from Iran (western borderlands) and Afghanistan, in the latter case including the destruction of irrigation schemes.

- **Potential effects of global climatic change.** It is beyond question that the composition of the world's atmosphere is being substantially altered as a result of human activities. A small but significant global warming has already been observed and is projected to continue. It is possible that this may lead to modifications to the general atmospheric circulation with consequent changes in rainfall.

These changes could be beneficial or adverse to land productivity or human welfare: specifically, in semi-arid regions, rainfall might become higher or lower, more reliable or less, or with lower or higher incidence of droughts. There is, however, no firm evidence of what such changes may be.

If adverse changes occur in some areas, then these will certainly constitute a most serious form of human-induced degradation of natural resources. It is accepted that, for a range of reasons, action should be taken to reduce emissions of 'greenhouse gases'. However, until there is clearer evidence, its potential effects upon climate must remain a matter of research, and these will not be further considered.

## PROBLEMS OF THE NATURAL ENVIRONMENT

**Aridity and drought**  'Aridity' and 'drought' are referred to in the ECOSOC resolution on which this study is based. These, however, are problems of the natural environment in semi-arid and arid areas. In the subsequent amplifications of the terms of reference it is clear that degradation, namely human-induced adverse environmental changes, is the intended focus. Therefore aridity and drought would only properly be included if it could be shown that rainfall had been reduced, or drought spells made more frequent, as a result of man's activities. This has not been established.

**Problem soils**  Soils which present special difficulties for agriculture may be called problem soils. They include saline soils, sandy soils, cracking clays, strongly acid soils, shallow soils, and soils on steeply sloping or poorly drained land. A comprehensive review for Asia and the Pacific is given in FAO/RAPA (1990) and a map of problem soils is in preparation.

To the extent that these are problems of the natural environment, problem soils do not constitute land degradation. However, land degradation frequently leads to an increase in the extent or severity of problem soils, for example, erosion causes shallow soils. A clear case is that of saline soils: these occur naturally, in which case they are problem soils, but their extent has been greatly increased by human-induced salinization.

## REVERSIBLE DEGRADATION AND LAND RECLAMATION

The effects of water and wind erosion are largely irreversible. Although plant nutrients and soil organic matter may be replaced, to replace the actual loss of soil material would require taking the soil out of use for many thousands of years, an impractical course of action.

In other cases, land degradation is reversible: soils with reduced organic matter can be restored by additions of plant residues, degraded pastures may recover under improved range management. Salinized soils can be restored to productive use, although at a high cost, through salinity control and reclamation projects.

Land reclamation frequently requires inputs which are costly, labour-demanding or both. The reclamation projects in salinized and waterlogged irrigated areas demonstrate this fact clearly. In other cases, the land can only be restored by taking it out of productive use for some years, as in reclamation forestry. The cost of reclamation, or restoration to productive use, of degraded soils is invariably less than the cost of preventing degradation before it occurs.

# Chapter 3

# Sources of data

## GLOBAL ASSESSMENT OF SOIL DEGRADATION (GLASOD)

Under an international project, *Global assessment of soil degradation (GLASOD)*, an attempt has been made for the first time to map the severity of degradation on a world scale, as the *World map of the status of human-induced soil degradation* (Oldeman *et al.*, 1990). The scale at the Equator is 1:15 000 000, becoming 1:13 000 000 at 30° latitude. The project was conducted by the International Soils Research and Information Centre (ISRIC) under the aegis of UNEP.

A standardized methodology, including definitions, was developed through international consultation. Data for individual countries was provided by the leading experts available, moderated by ISRIC with the aim of standardization. The GLASOD assessment (as it will be called) includes all the types of land degradation covered in the present study, somewhat differently subdivided but in ways that are compatible with the classification adopted here. This last feature is of the highest value for filling what would otherwise be gaps in data from other sources.

At the same time, the authors of GLASOD acknowledge that there are certainly deficiencies in this first output, and that the World Map should be regarded as a first approximation. For some countries of South Asia, there exist other estimates, mainly governmental, of the extent of degradation, derived by somewhat different means. This range of sources provides the opportunity to compare data with the objectives first, of seeing how consistent these are, and secondly, to obtain best estimates.

For these reasons, it was decided in the present study:

1.  To take the GLASOD classification of types of degradation as the basis for development of that used here, which is simplified and partly regrouped. The equivalence between GLASOD types and those of the present survey is given in Table 3.

2.  To adopt the GLASOD definitions for degrees of severity of degradation (see below).

3.  To treat the GLASOD assessments of the extent of degradation as a starting point or standard, against which other estimates can be compared; but not necessarily to adopt them as the best estimates where evidence suggests otherwise.

TABLE 3
**Correspondence between GLASOD types of degradation and those of the present study**

| This study | GLASOD* | |
|---|---|---|
| Water erosion | Wt | Loss of topsoil |
| | Wd | Terrain deformation/mass movement |
| Wind erosion | Et | Loss of topsoil |
| | Ed | Terrain deformation |
| | Eo | Overblowing |
| Soil fertility decline | Cn | Loss of nutrients and/or organic matter |
| | Ca | Acidification |
| | Pc | Compaction, sealing and crusting |
| Salinization | Cs | Salinization |
| Waterlogging | Pw | Waterlogging |
| Lowering of the groundwater table | Pa | Aridification |

\*   The GLASOD classes of **Eo** overblowing, **Cp** pollution, and **Fs** subsidence of organic soils were not reported for map units of South Asia. The class **Pa** aridification was included Guidelines for the GLASOD study and reported on South Asia Data sheets, but is not included in GLASOD maps.

TABLE 4
**GLASOD definitions of degrees of degradation**

The degree to which the soil is presently degraded is estimated in relation to changes in agricultural suitability, in relation to declined productivity and in some cases in relation to its biotic functions. Four levels are recognized:

**1. Light:**      The terrain has somewhat reduced agricultural suitability, but is suitable for use in local farming systems. Restoration to full productivity is possible by modifications of the management system. Original biotic functions are still largely intact.

**2. Moderate:**   The terrain has greatly reduced agricultural productivity, but is still suitable for use in local farming systems. Major improvements are required to restore productivity. Original biotic functions are partially destroyed.

**3. Strong:**     The terrain is non reclaimable at farm level. Major engineering works are required for terrain restoration. Original biotic functions are largely destroyed.

**4. Extreme:**    The terrain is unreclaimable and beyond restoration. Original biotic functions are fully destroyed.

In the present study these same definitions are employed, but are referred to as "degree", "degree of severity" or "severity of degradation", all with the same meaning.

## Degrees of severity of degradation

As will be made clear in later discussion, the definition of the degree, or severity, of degradation is of the highest importance. The definitions used in the present study are the same as those of degrees of degradation in GLASOD. In the present state of knowledge they are necessarily non-quantitative, although they contain guidelines for quantification.

In view of the importance of these definitions, they are given in full in Table 4. In abbreviated form the degrees of degradation are:

Light:          somewhat reduced agricultural productivity.
Moderate:       greatly reduced agricultural productivity.
Strong:         unreclaimable at farm level.
Extreme:        unreclaimable and impossible to restore (with present technology).

The class 'Extreme' was not reported for any map unit in South Asia (one data sheet contained it originally, reduced on moderation to 'Strong').

In terms of their effects, the farmer is still using land with light and moderate degrees of degradation, but the boundary with strong degradation is the point at which land use has to be abandoned. Light degradation may not be clearly visible, but the farmer knows that yields (or other production) are lower than they might otherwise have been, or that additional inputs are necessary. Moderate degradation will often be visibly apparent, including stunted crops or sparsely vegetated rangeland, and yields are clearly and substantially lower. By definition, strong degradation means that the land has been abandoned, and no longer has potential for production.[1]

## Data for South Asia

For reason of cartographic necessity, the GLASOD World Map shows only the dominant form of degradation (as severity times extent) as coloured mapped areas, with the secondary form shown in the map symbol. Where, as happened widely, three or more forms of degradation were reported for the same map unit, only the first two appear on the map. This results in gaps when an attempt is made to abstract one form of degradation, say wind erosion, for all areas. This situation has recently been improved by the printing of maps of individual kinds of degradation, at a smaller scale, in the *World atlas of desertification* (UNEP, 1992a).

As part of the collaborative input to the present project, however, the complete original data sheets were made available, together with associated country maps and correspondence. These contain substantially more information than the published maps. Each data sheet (known as matrix tables) refers to a delineated map unit. For the unit, it gives:

□   background information: physiography, soils, geology, climate, population, land use, vegetation;
□   area of the map unit (square kilometres);
□   a list of all types of land degradation identified, giving for each its type, degree (severity), extent (as percentage of the map unit affected), present rate, and principal causes;
□   remarks, on each type and on the unit as whole.

---

[1]   In terms of land suitability classification (FAO, 1976), light degree might have the effect of a lowering by one suitability subclass (e.g. S1 to S2, highly to moderately suitable), moderate degradation a lowering by two subclasses (e.g. S1 to S3, highly to marginally suitable), whilst strong degradation means that the class boundary between S and N, suitable and not suitable, has been crossed.

Data on extent are given as five classes on a quasi-geometric scale, with bounds of 5, 10, 25 and 50%. For the present study these were converted to a central value (using the geometric mean) and multiplied by the area of the unit to give a best estimate of the area affected by the type of degradation.

Treating one map unit with, say, 3 types of degradation as 3 records, and omitting units with no degradation, available data is as follows:

| Country | Number of map units | Number of records |
|---|---|---|
| Afghanistan | 17 | 26 |
| Bangladesh | 4 | 7 |
| Bhutan | 0 | 0 |
| India | 26 | 33 |
| Iran | 59 | 103 |
| Nepal | 4 | 7 |
| Pakistan | 28 | 46 |
| Sri Lanka | 9 | 27 |

The records were put into a relational database, reviewed to remove errors, and analysed.

ISRIC/UNEP provided specially prepared maps showing the extent and severity of each type of degradation for the eight countries of South Asia.

### Treatment of Bhutan

There are no GLASOD data sheets for Bhutan. The world map appears to treat this by extrapolation of conditions reported from adjacent countries to west and east, and the first procedure tried was to abstract this information and construct data sheets. However, this gave an estimate of area affected by water erosion over twice that of the FAO figure for total area under crops and pasture.

Whilst extrapolation is applicable to the physiographic zones, Bhutan has a much lower population density. It is reported that whilst there is a high hazard of erosion, including landsliding, "environmental planning precedes, and thereby hopefully prevents, environmental degradation" (Bhutan National Environmental Secretariat, 1992). It would be possible to assign zero degradation to the country, but this might give a false impression that no problem existed.

After discussion with FAO staff who have visited the country, a working assumption was made. This is that 10% of the reported area under crops and pasture is affected by water erosion, of which 9% is light and 1% strong, the latter representing landslides and gullies. This is intended to convert into figures the reported situation that the problem is not presently severe, but exists and should be guarded against in the future.

The total area is so small that this assumption does not appreciably affect regional totals. No other type of degradation has been reported for Bhutan.

### *The GLASOD assessment: results*

In the presentation of results, for the purpose of broad regional comparison the countries have been grouped into a dry zone, with predominantly semi-arid and arid climates, and humid zone countries. Using the database, India was divided into dry and humid regions, the dry region being taken as all map units with rainfall not exceeding 750 mm per year (mainly the State of Rajasthan and western parts of Harayana, Gujerat and Punjab). Thus *dry zone* refers to Afghanistan, Iran, Pakistan and the dry region of India, *humid zone* to Bangladesh, Bhutan, Nepal, Sri Lanka and the humid region of India.

In the tables, areas are given in units of 1000 hectares. For discussion in the text, values are for the most part rounded to millions of hectares.

It should be noted that whilst "severity" is used in a specialized sense on the GLASOD map legend, in the present study, "degree", "degree of severity" and "severity" of degradation are all used with the same meaning.

### Other sources of data

The starting point for estimates of the type, severity and extent of degradation is the report of the regional expert consultation *Environmental issues in land and water development* (FAO/RAPA, 1992). This includes a regional overview, and country reports for Bangladesh, India, Nepal, Pakistan and Sri Lanka. Other recent reviews containing data for more than one type of degradation are FAO/RAPA (1990) and ESCAP (1990a). Data for Afghanistan and Bhutan are qualitative only, and were obtained mainly from the respective UNCED reports (Afghanistan, Ministry of Planning, 1992; Bhutan, National Environmental Secretariat, 1992). Data sources for specific types of degradation are cited in context below. A valuable recent guide to sources of environmental data is the annotated bibliography *1992 Directory of country environmental studies* (World Resources Institute, 1992).

Most of these data ultimately derive from surveys or estimates by Government institutions: soil survey, soil conservation and irrigation management departments. Most of these estimates were initially obtained with care and effort, either from surveys or by assembly of estimates submitted by state and district branches and officers. They suffer, however, from *a failure properly to define the degree of severity of the degradation for which an area is reported*. As a consequence, different estimates may vary by a factor of two, or sometimes more.

The same data may be copied many times. Secondary publications sometimes do not make clear their sources (or even, in a few instances, units!). For all these other sources the data are highly non-uniform, both in availability and nature, as between the countries of the region.

For these reasons, the decision was made to take the GLASOD survey as a standard, which is then compared with other estimates. Only where there appears to be clear evidence of a data bias in the GLASOD survey have its results been modified from other sources to obtain best estimates as used in the present study.

**Variations in data and the need for definition of degrees of severity**

A major finding of the present comparative review is that large variations exist between different estimates of areas affected by degradation. A lack of surveys, and different methods used, is a contributory factor to this problem. The major cause, however, is believed to be the lack of precision in defining what is being surveyed.

# Chapter 4

# Status of degradation. I. Erosion and fertility decline

**WATER EROSION** (Tables 5 and 6, Figures 2 and 3)

According to the GLASOD assessment, a total of 83 M ha is assessed as affected by water erosion in the region, or 25% of the total area under crops and pasture. This is made up of 33 M ha with light erosion, 36 M ha moderate and 13 M ha strong erosion. The dry zone is most affected with 39% of the area under crops and pasture, compared with 18% for the humid zone.

The countries most seriously affected are in absolute area India and Iran, and relative to crops and pasture, Iran, Sri Lanka and Nepal. Examples where erosion has reached the severe degree, leading to abandonment of land, include parts of the hill areas of Sri Lanka (Stocking, 1992; Sri Lanka, Natural Resources, Energy and Science Authority, 1991, p.120), and the Pothwar Plateau of the Punjab region of Pakistan[1] (Nizami and Shafiq, 1990). For current erosion under inappropriate land use, there are many estimates in excess of 100 t/ha per year, including for parts of India, Nepal and Sri Lanka (e.g. Das *et al.*, 1991; Stocking, 1992).

The map shows a clear relation to physiographic units. Most affected are the populated mountain regions of the Himalaya-Hindu Kush, the mountainous rim of Iran, and the areas of predominantly rainfed agriculture of the Deccan of India (with the Western Ghats most seriously affected) and Sri Lanka. Also affected are strips where the Gangetic river system has cut into terraces, whilst ravines are widespread along the rivers Jumna and Chambal.

Table 6 shows some estimates of areas affected by water erosion, giving the words used to define the areas stated. For *India*, the earlier estimates are in the range 69-127 M ha, which is 2-4 times the GLASOD estimate. The figure of 4 M ha under gullies or ravines has frequently been quoted, and is one third that of the GLASOD value for strong degradation. The estimate of Sehgal and Abrol (1992) is a new assessment by the National Bureau of Soil Survey and Land Use Planning "following the criteria and guidelines of the GLASOD methodology". The value is over twice the original GLASOD estimate. For *Pakistan*, the totals are of the same magnitude, 11.2 as compared with 7.2 M ha.

These comparisons illustrate what will be found repeatedly, that estimates of areas affected by land degradation show a wide range of values.

---

[1]   This area has deep silty soils.  Some of the erosion may have originated under natural conditions, although undoubtedly accelerated by human action.

TABLE 5
**GLASOD assessment: areas affected by water erosion**

Unit: 1000 ha

| | Light | Moderate | Strong | Total | Total as percent of agricultural land |
|---|---|---|---|---|---|
| Afghanistan | 8 560 | 2 597 | 0 | 11 156 | 29% |
| Bangladesh | 0 | 1 504 | 0 | 1 504 | 15% |
| Bhutan | 36 | 0 | 4 | 40 | 10% |
| India | 2 936 | 17 217 | 12 620 | 32 773 | 18% |
| Iran | 14 504 | 11 896 | 0 | 26 400 | 45% |
| Nepal | 520 | 1 072 | 0 | 1 592 | 34% |
| Pakistan | 6 080 | 1 124 | 0 | 7 204 | 28% |
| Sri Lanka | 72 | 157 | 845 | 1 074 | 46% |
| India, dry region | 1 177 | 0 | 1 676 | 2 853 | - |
| India, humid region | 1 759 | 17 217 | 10 944 | 29 920 | - |
| Dry zone | 30 320 | 15 617 | 1 676 | 47 613 | 32% |
| Humid zone | 2 387 | 19 951 | 11 791 | 34 130 | 20% |
| Region | 32 707 | 35 568 | 13 468 | 81 743 | 25% |

TABLE 6
**Country estimates of areas affected by water erosion**

| Country | Description | Area (Mha) | Source |
|---|---|---|---|
| India | Problem area due to erosion | 127 | RAPA (1992, p. 196) |
| | Affected by water erosion | 111 | RAPA (1992, p. 195) |
| | Severely eroded <u>and</u> | 106 | |
| | At critical stage of degradation (water & wind erosion) | 69 | Das (1977) |
| | Eroded | 74 | Society for Promotion of Wastelands Development (1984) |
| | Gullies | 4 | Das (1977); India, National Land Use and Conservation Board (1988) |
| | Water erosion | 87 | Sehgal and Abrol (1992) |
| Pakistan | Slightly eroded | 0.4 | Mian and Javed (1989) |
| | Moderately eroded | 3.6 | RAPA (1990, p. 229) |
| | Severely eroded | 3.7 | |
| | Very severely eroded | 3.4 | |
| | Total eroded | 11.2 | |

In terms of total area affected, water erosion is the most serious problem of land degradation in the region. It is the only degradation type which is widely found both in the dry and humid zones.

As the basis for discussion in the remainder of this report, **the GLASOD estimates for water erosion are accepted**, whilst noting that for India, it is possible that they are 2-3 times higher.

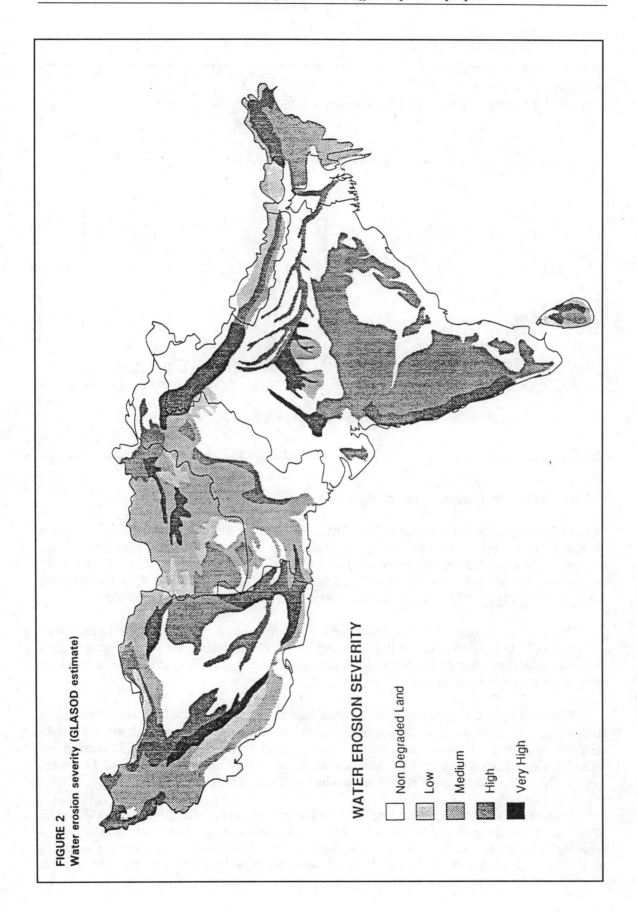

**FIGURE 2**
**Water erosion severity (GLASOD estimate)**

**WATER EROSION SEVERITY**

Non Degraded Land

Low

Medium

High

Very High

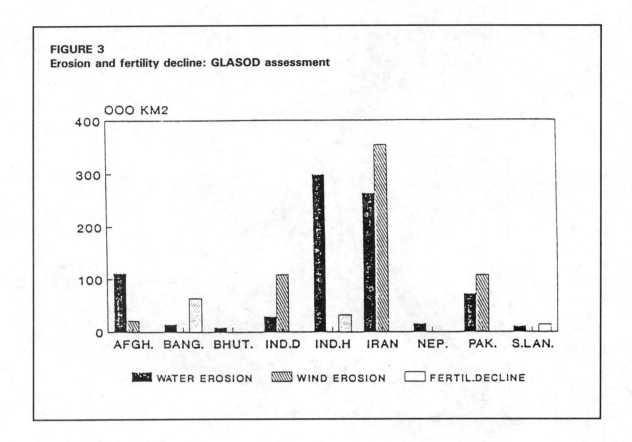

FIGURE 3
Erosion and fertility decline: GLASOD assessment

## WIND EROSION (Tables 7 and 8, Figures 3 and 4)

In the GLASOD estimate, a total of 59 M ha is assessed as affected by wind erosion in the region, lying entirely within the dry zone. Within this zone, 48% of land under crops and pasture is affected. This is predominantly, 34 M ha, of moderate degree. It is very unevenly represented by countries, affecting 60% of agricultural land in Iran and 42% in Pakistan, whilst the dry region of India has the same total area affected, 11 M ha, as Pakistan.

The map illustrates this clear and expected localization in the dry belt stretching from central Iran to the Thar Desert of Pakistan and India. The irrigated belt of the Indus system cuts a swathe through the affected zone, with wind erosion occurring along the unirrigated belts between river systems.

The relatively low proportion of Afghanistan mapped as affected by wind erosion is surprising, although the high altitude and consequent lower evapotranspiration of its low-rainfall areas may be partly responsible. The national report to the UNCED conference states, "desertification and erosion continue unabated" (Afghanistan, Ministry of Planning, 1992). This situation requires clarification when political conditions permit.

Table 8 shows country estimates. For *India*, one estimate is similar to the GLASOD total, the others three times higher. For Pakistan, the country estimate is about half that of GLASOD. However, a recent land use survey of the whole country includes the mapping units, "range land, non-degraded" and "range land, degraded"; by inspection, it appears that

TABLE 7
**GLASOD assessment: areas affected by wind erosion**

Unit: 1000 ha

|  | Light | Moderate | Strong | Total | Total as percent of agricultural land |
|---|---|---|---|---|---|
| Afghanistan | 1 873 | 0 | 209 | 2 082 | 5% |
| Bangladesh | 0 | 0 | 0 | 0 | 0% |
| Bhutan | 0 | 0 | 0 | 0 | 0% |
| India | 0 | 1 754 | 9 042 | 10 796 | 6% |
| Iran | 6 559 | 25 730 | 3 085 | 35 374 | 60% |
| Nepal | 0 | 0 | 0 | 0 | 0% |
| Pakistan | 3 998 | 6 742 | 0 | 10 740 | 42% |
| Sri Lanka | 0 |  | 0 | 0 | 0% |
| India, dry region | 0 | 1 754 | 9 042 | 10 796 | - |
| India, humid region | 0 | 0 | 0 | 0 | - |
| Dry zone | 12 430 | 34 225 | 12 337 | 58 992 | 39% |
| Humid zone | 0 | 0 | 0 | 0 | 0% |
| Region | 12 430 | 34 225 | 12 337 | 58 992 | 18% |

TABLE 8
**Country estimates of areas affected by wind erosion**

| Country | Description | Area (Mha) | Source |
|---|---|---|---|
| India | Affected by wind erosion | 12.9 | Society for the Promotion of Wasteland Development (1984) |
|  | Subject to wind erosion | 38.7 | RAPA (1992, p. 195) |
|  | Subject to wind erosion | 32.0 | Das (1977) |
|  | Subject to wind erosion | 17.7 | Sehgal and Abrol (1992) |
| Pakistan | Slightly eroded | 2.6 | Mian and Javed (1989) |
|  | Moderately eroded | 0.5 | RAPA (1992, p. 363) |
|  | Severely eroded | 1.6 |  |
|  | Total eroded | 4.8 |  |

over 90%, possibly 95%, of range land is considered to be degraded (Asian Development Bank, 1992b).

As the basis for discussion in the remainder of this report, **the GLASOD estimates for wind erosion are accepted**.

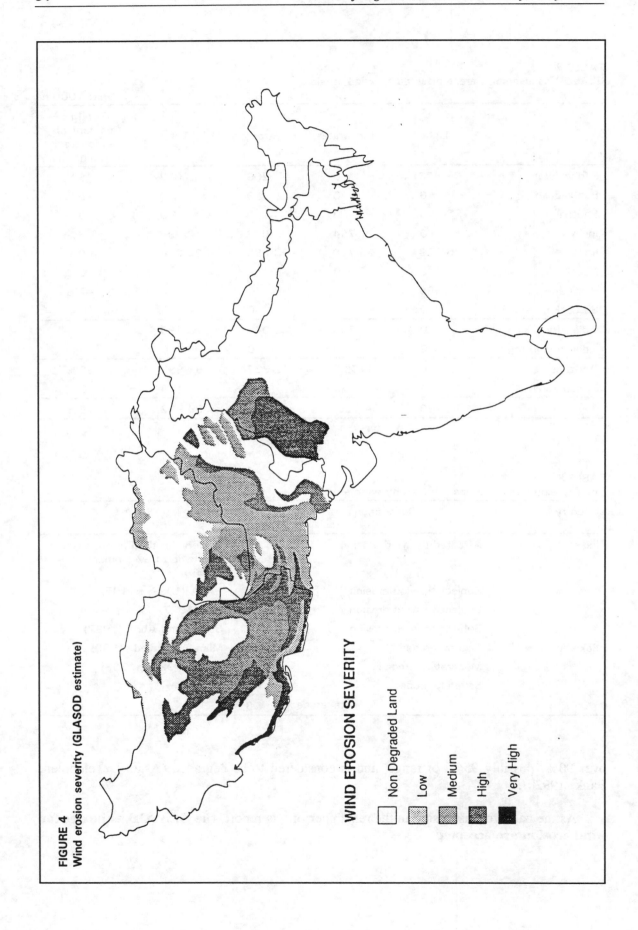

**FIGURE 4**
**Wind erosion severity (GLASOD estimate)**

**WIND EROSION SEVERITY**

Non Degraded Land
Low
Medium
High
Very High

## SOIL FERTILITY DECLINE (Tables 9 and 10, Figure 3)

### The GLASOD estimate

GLASOD defines this form of degradation as "loss of nutrients and/or organic matter. The GLASOD assessment shows 65% of agricultural land in Bangladesh and 61% in Sri Lanka affected by this type of degradation. No other areas are reported apart from three map units in India, described on the data sheets as having "heavy leaching with lateritic crust formation". However, a recent country analysis of the GLASOD results gives a much larger value of 26 200 ha (Sehgal and Abrol, 1992).

It is clear that there is a reporting bias here. The respondents for Bangladesh and Sri Lanka recognize this form of degradation as being widespread on cropland, both rainfed and irrigated, whilst those for other countries of the humid zone initially did not (but see below). Evidence of the existence of this form of degradation calls for discussion.

### Evidence for soil fertility decline

Over the past 30 years there has been a large increase in fertilizer consumption in the region, associated with the introduction of high-yielding crop varieties. Bangladesh, India, Iran, Pakistan and Sri Lanka all now apply on average more than 70 kg/ha nutrients. This has been a major factor in the increase in crop yields over the period.

However, an inter-related set of soil fertility problems has been reported, directly or indirectly associated with fertilizer application. An early report is from 1981 (Bowonder, 1981) and evidence is accumulating. These problems are as follows.

**Organic matter depletion** Crop residues are widely used as fuel and fodder, and not returned to the soil. This results in a decrease in soil organic matter content. In Bangladesh, the average organic matter (presumably of topsoils) is said to have declined by 50%, from 2% to 1%, over the past 20 years (Bangladesh, 1992). For the Indian State of Harayana, soil test reports over 15 years show a decrease in soil carbon (Chaudhary and Aneja, 1991). Decreased organic matter leads to:

◻ degradation of soil physical properties, including water holding capacity, as has developed in India (Indian Council of Agricultural Research, personal communication);
◻ reduced nutrient retention capacity;
◻ lower release of nutrients, including micronutrients, from mineralization of organic matter.

As a consequence of all these effects, there may be lower response to fertilizer.

**A continuing negative soil nutrient balance** Removal of nutrients from the soil in crop harvest appears substantially to exceed inputs as natural replacement and fertilizers. Negative soil nutrient balances have been reported for all three major nutrients in Bangladesh and Nepal; for phosphorus and potassium in Sri Lanka, and a large deficit for potassium in Pakistan (FAO, 1986b). Nutrient depletion has been reported for each of the 15 agro-climatic regions of India (Biswas and Tewatia, 1991; Tandon, 1992, citing other sources). For India, a deficiency between nutrient removal and addition of 60 kg/ha per year, or 9 Mt for the whole country, has been estimated (Tandon, 1992).

TABLE 9
**GLASOD assessment: areas affected by soil fertility decline***

Unit: 1000 ha

| | Light | Moderate | Strong | Total | Total as percent of agricultural land |
|---|---|---|---|---|---|
| Afghanistan | 0 | 0 | 0 | 0 | 0% |
| Bangladesh | 6 367 | 0 | 0 | 6 367 | 65% |
| Bhutan | 0 | 0 | 0 | 0 | 0% |
| India | 0 | 0 | 3 183 | 3 183 | 2% |
| Iran | 0 | 0 | 0 | 0 | 0% |
| Nepal | 0 | 0 | 0 | 0 | 0% |
| Pakistan | 0 | 0 | 0 | 0 | 0% |
| Sri Lanka | 693 | 731 | 0 | 1 425 | 61% |
| India, dry region | 0 | 0 | 0 | 0 | - |
| India, humid region | 0 | 0 | 3 183 | 3 183 | - |
| Dry zone | 0 | 0 | 0 | 0 | 0% |
| Humid zone | 7 060 | 731 | 3 183 | 10 974 | 6% |
| Region | 7 060 | 731 | 3 183 | 10 974 | 3% |

*    Described in GLASOD as "Loss of nutrients and/or organic matter".

TABLE 10
**Soil fertility decline: revised estimates**

Unit: 1000 ha

| | Light | Moderate | Strong | Total | Total as percent of agricultural land |
|---|---|---|---|---|---|
| India | 26 200* | 0 | 3 183 | 29 383 | 16% |
| Pakistan | 5 200 | 0 | 0 | 5 200 | 20% |

*    Of which 2 200 are attributed to the dry region.

**Imbalance in fertilizer application**    Fertilizer use in the region is dominated by nitrogen; N:P and N:K ratios are higher than in the other parts of the world. For example, the N:P:K ratio for India is 1.00 : 0.33 : 0.17 compared with 1.00 : 0.52 : 0.40 for the world (FAO data; Pradhan, 1992). This trend originated in the early years of the 'green revolution'. When fertilizers are first applied to a soil, a high response is frequently obtained from nitrogen. The improved crop growth depletes the soil of other nutrients; "In such systems, nitrogen is simply used as a shovel to mine the soil of other nutrients" (Tandon, 1992). Long-term experiments in India show depletion of soil P and K are higher for plots with N fertilizer, and depletion of K still higher with N+P fertilizer (Tandon, 1992). In Pakistan, use of nitrogen (mainly as urea) is still increasing, whereas use of phosphorus has levelled off in the last 5 years, and very little potassium or micronutrient fertilizers are applied (Twyford, 1994).

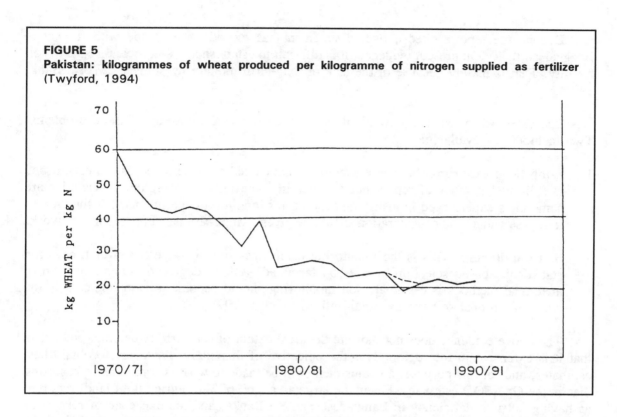

**FIGURE 5**
**Pakistan: kilogrammes of wheat produced per kilogramme of nitrogen supplied as fertilizer** (Twyford, 1994)

**Secondary and micronutrient deficiencies** An increasing incidence of sulphur and zinc deficiency is occurring in the region. Sulphur deficiency has been reported for India, Pakistan and Sri Lanka, and zinc deficiency for India and Pakistan (FAO/RAPA, 1992, p.65; Bowonder, 1981; Chaudhary and Aneja, 1991; Abrol, 1990). For Bangladesh, 3.9 M ha are reported deficient in sulphur and 1.75 M ha in zinc, including areas of continuous swamp rice cultivation (Bangladesh, 1992; Shaheed, 1992). Pakistan, because of its generally alkaline soils, is particularly liable to micronutrient deficiencies, which are being increasingly reported (Twyford, 1994).

**Failure of increases in fertilizer use to be matched by increases in crop yield** A levelling off, or plateau, in the crop yield increases which took place in the 1960s and 1970s is found in many countries of the region. The situation is clearly illustrated by data for Pakistan, where more or less linear increases in fertilizer nutrient use have not been equalled by rates of yield increase for wheat, rice and sugar cane (Figure 5). There may be several reasons for this serious effect, but a major contributory factor is undoubtedly decline in soil productivity (Chaudhary and Aneja, 1991).

**Lower responses to fertilizers** Long-term experiments in India have shown low or zero response to N fertilizer under severe P deficiency, and a low (and uneconomic) response to N-P-K fertilizer where there is zinc deficiency (Tandon, 1992). A striking example is a 33-year fertilizer experiment at Ranchi, Bihar; despite changes to improved varieties, wheat yields have declined substantially over the period with N, NP and NPK fertilization, whereas they have risen with farmyard manure (Goswami and Rattan, 1992).

Despite the reports cited above, a statement has recently been made with respect to Bangladesh that, "On present evidence, it is difficult to establish any significant trends in soil fertility. That is mainly because of the lack of long-term monitoring studies" (World Bank, 1991).

The existence of such a view highlights the urgent need for study of these problems. Two methods are available:

1.   **Long-term experiments**  These should be maintained or, where necessary, established at a limited number of representative sites in countries of the region. Difficulties are sometimes experienced in justifying funding for long-term experiments, but they are of immense value, and consideration should be given to international support for a network.

2.   **Soil monitoring**  This is the monitoring of changes in soil properties over time, on a statistically-based selection of sites on farmland. A high degree of standardization of analytical methods is essential. Soil monitoring should become a major element in the work of national soil survey organizations (Young, 1991).

The above evidence does not indicate the areal extent of soil fertility decline, other than that it is extensive in the region. It is the objective of this study, however, to obtain best estimates, and for this purpose, an adjustment will be made to what is considered a reporting bias in the GLASOD estimates. Given the large areas (60-65% of agricultural land) reported as having nutrient deficiency in Bangladesh and Sri Lanka, and the existence of reports as outlined above, it is tentatively, and conservatively, estimated that an additional 20% of the agricultural land of both India and Pakistan are affected by soil fertility decline, at least to a light degree.

**Revised country estimates**  Whilst soil fertility decline was shown for *India* only for a small area, as the above evidence has accumulated its greater extent has been accepted. A recent estimate gives 26.2 M ha as affected by loss of nutrients. There is no corresponding estimate for Pakistan, but evidence of the widespread occurrence of fertility decline is equally strong.

Consequently, as the basis for the rest of this report, **the GLASOD estimates for soil fertility decline are revised for India and Pakistan, as in Table 10.**

# Chapter 5

# Status of degradation. II. Other types of degradation and summary

**WATERLOGGING** (Tables 11 and 12, Figure 6)

Waterlogging is the rise of the water table into the root zone of the soil profile, such that plant growth is adversely affected by deficiency of oxygen. The critical depth depends on the kind of crop, but waterlogging is commonly defined as light for a soil profile depth of 3 m for substantial parts of the year, and moderate for less than 1.5 m. The severe degree occurs with a water table at 0-30 cm depth, and also included in this study is ponding, where it rises above the surface.

Waterlogging as a form of land degradation should be distinguished from naturally occurring poorly drained areas, and also from the different problem of flooding, which is noted below.

In the GLASOD estimate, waterlogging affects 4.6 M ha, largely in the irrigated areas of India and Pakistan. It is closely linked with salinization. In Iran it occurs in the coastal zone. The progressive rise in the water table beneath the Indo-Gangetic plains since the commencement of large scale irrigation schemes in the 1930s has been monitored (e.g. Ahmad and Kutcher, 1992).

TABLE 11
**GLASOD assessment: areas affected by waterlogging**

Unit: 1000 ha

|  | Light | Moderate | Strong | Total | Total as percent of agricultural land |
|---|---|---|---|---|---|
| Afghanistan | 0 | 0 | 0 | 0 | 0% |
| Bangladesh | 0 | 0 | 0 | 0 | 0% |
| Bhutan | 0 | 0 | 0 | 0 | 0% |
| India | 0 | 3 083 | 0 | 3 083 | 2% |
| Iran | 551 | 0 | 0 | 551 | 1% |
| Nepal | 0 | 0 | 0 | 0 | 0% |
| Pakistan | 965 | 0 | 0 | 965 | 4% |
| Sri Lanka | 0 | 0 | 0 | 0 | 0% |
| India, dry region | 0 | 3 083 | 0 | 3 083 | - |
| India, humid region | 0 | 0 | 0 | 0 | - |
| Dry zone | 1 516 | 3 083 | 0 | 4 599 | 3% |
| Humid zone | 0 | 0 | 0 | 0 | 0% |
| Region | 1 516 | 3 083 | 0 | 4 599 | 1% |

TABLE 12A
**Country estimates of areas affected by waterlogging**

| Country | W.T. Depth (cm) | Area (100 ha) | Source |
|---|---|---|---|
| India | Waterlogging | 8 530 | RAPA (1992, p. 195) |
| India | Waterlogging | 7 000 | Sehgal and Abrol (1992) |
| Pakistan | 200-100 | 2 507 | Ahmad and Kutcher (1992, p. 42) |
|  | 100-0 | 1 170 |  |
|  | Total | 3 676 |  |
| Pakistan | 100-150 | 318 | Mian and Javed (1989) quoting data of Soil Survey of Pakistan |
|  | 50-100 | 293 |  |
|  | 0-50 | 816 |  |
|  | 0-150 (saline soil) | 127 |  |
|  | Total | 1 554 |  |
| Pakistan | 0-150 | 2 120 | Ibid., quoting data of WAPDA |
| Pakistan | 0-150 | 2 068 | Ibid., quoting detailed survey of 1978 |

TABLE 12B
**Revised estimates of areas affected by waterlogging**

| Country | Degree | Area (1000 ha) |
|---|---|---|
| Pakistan | Light | 800 |
|  | Moderate | 400 |
|  | Severe | 800 |
|  | Total | 2 000 |

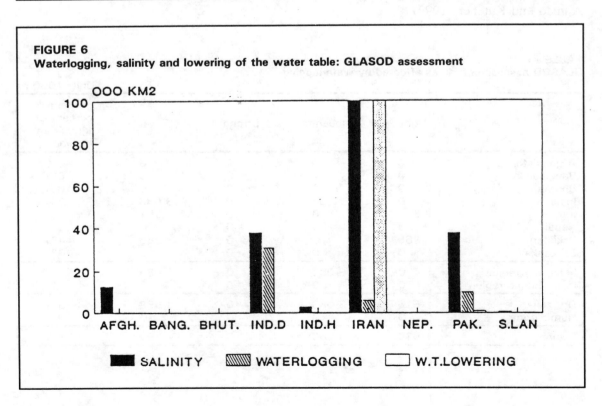

FIGURE 6
**Waterlogging, salinity and lowering of the water table: GLASOD assessment**

Country estimates are given in Table 12A. For India, the figure given is more than twice the GLASOD estimate. For Pakistan, four sources quoted give total areas affected of 3.7, 1.6, 2.1 and 2.1 M ha, compared with the GLASOD value of 0.96 M ha. Since the Pakistan country data come from at least two independent surveys, show good agreement (relative to the standards found for other types of degradation!) and are believed to result from detailed field surveys, the country estimates are preferred.

For the purpose of subsequent discussion, **the GLASOD estimates of areas affected by waterlogging are accepted for all countries except Pakistan, for which they are modified as in Table 12B.**

## SALINIZATION (Tables 13 and 14, Figures 6 and 7)

The generalized term *salinization* is employed here to cover all changes to soils involving the increase of salt, including both salinization in the narrow sense, the increase of free salts, and sodification, the saturation of the exchange complex with sodium. The following definitions are in common use:

|                            | ECe (mS/cm) | pH       | ESP (%) |
|----------------------------|-------------|----------|---------|
| Saline soils               | > 2         | < 8.2    | < 15    |
| Sodic (or non-saline sodic)| < 2         | > 8.2    | > 15    |
| Saline-sodic               | > 2         | variable | > 15    |

ECe = electrical conductivity of the saturation extract
ESP = exchangeable sodium percentage

Note:    limiting values of ECe 4 mS/cm and pH 8.5 were formerly used.

In the GLASOD estimate, the region is estimated to have 42 M ha affected by salinization, nearly all in the dry zone. Of this, 33 M ha are in Iran, where more than half of all agricultural land is shown as being affected. There are approximately 4 M ha in both India and Pakistan. In relation to irrigated land, the percentage affected appears as 10% for India, 23% for Pakistan and 9% for Sri Lanka, although these values should be reduced since some of the salinization results from saline intrusion into unirrigated land.

The values for strong salinization are important, for this by definition refers to land abandoned from cultivation. The area affected is 10 M ha of which 8 M ha are in Iran and 2 M ha in India. The absence of strong salinization from areas of Pakistan under similar irrigation and land management systems to those of India suggests a reporting bias.

The map shows a clear localization in two situations, irrigated land and coastal zones. A dry coastal strip along much of Iran through Pakistan to Gujarat in India is affected, in part by saline intrusion. The other areas heavily affected are the Central basin areas of Iran and the irrigation systems of the Indo-Gangetic plains.

TABLE 13
**GLASOD assessment: areas affected by salinization**

Unit: 1000 ha

|  | Light | Moderate | Strong | Total | Total as percent of agricultural land |
|---|---|---|---|---|---|
| Afghanistan | 1 271 | 0 | 0 | 1 271 | 3% |
| Bangladesh | 0 | 0 | 0 | 0 | 0% |
| Bhutan | 0 | 0 | 0 | 0 | 0% |
| India | 0 | 2 111 | 2 033 | 4 144 | 2% |
| Iran | 10 099 | 14 272 | 8 301 | 32 672 | 55% |
| Nepal | 0 | 0 | 0 | 0 | 0% |
| Pakistan | 3 457 | 377 | 0 | 3 834 | 15% |
| Sri Lanka | 47 | 0 | 0 | 47 | 2% |
| India, dry region | 0 | 2 111 | 1 695 | 3 806 | - |
| India, humid region | 0 | 0 | 338 | 338 | - |
| Dry zone | 14 828 | 16 759 | 9 996 | 41 583 | 28% |
| Humid zone | 48 | 0 | 338 | 386 | 0.2% |
| Region | 14 828 | 16 759 | 10 335 | 41 969 | 13% |

TABLE 14A
**Country estimates of areas affected by salinization**

| Country | Szabolcs (1979) | RAPA (1988) | Dent *et al.* (1992) | Massoud (1977) | Pannamperuma and Bandyopadhyay (1980) |
|---|---|---|---|---|---|
| Afghanistan | 3.10 | NA | NA | 3.1 | NA |
| Bangladesh | 3.02 | NA | 1.30 | 3.0 | 3.70 |
| India* | 23.80 | 7.00 | 7.04 | 23.8 | 26.10 |
| Iran | 27.08 | NA | 21.10 | 27.1 | NA |
| Pakistan | 10.46 | 10.50 | 12.00 | 10.50 | 10.50 |
| Sri Lanka | 0.20 | 0.16 | 0.70 | NA | NA |

NA: Not assessed.
*    For India, a further estimate of 6Mha is given by Sehgal and Abrol (1992).

TABLE 14B
**Estimates of areas affected by salinization, Pakistan**

| Country | Description | Area (Mha) | Source |
|---|---|---|---|
| India | Surface/patchy salinity and sodicity | 0.6 |  |
|  | Gypsiferous saline/saline-sodic soils | 0.7 | Mian and Javed (1989) quoting data of Soil Survey of Pakistan |
|  | Porous saline-sodic soils | 1.8 |  |
|  | Dense saline-sodic soils | 1.2 |  |
| Pakistan | Total | 5.3 |  |
|  | Slightly saline | 1.9 | Mian and Javed (1989) quoting data of Water and Power Development Authority |
|  | Moderately saline | 1.0 |  |
|  | Strongly saline | 1.3 |  |
|  | Total | 4.2 |  |

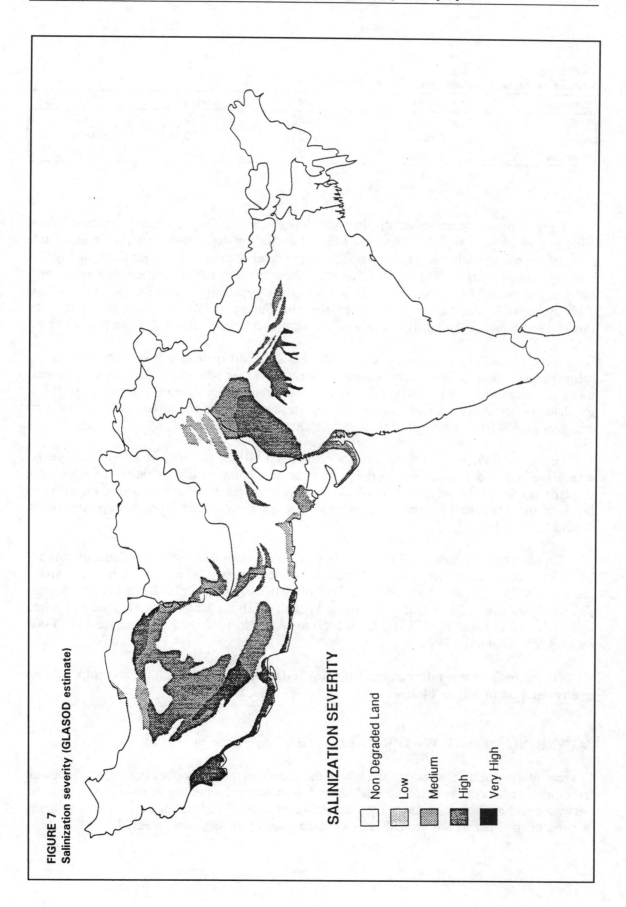

**FIGURE 7**
**Salinization severity (GLASOD estimate)**

**SALINIZATION SEVERITY**

☐ Non Degraded Land

▨ Low

▨ Medium

▨ High

■ Very High

TABLE 14C
**Revised estimates of areas affected by salinization**

| Country | Light | Moderate | Strong | Total |
|---|---|---|---|---|
| India | 0 | 3 500 | 3 500 | 7 000 |
| Iran | 5 000 | 7 000 | 4 000 | 16 000 |
| Pakistan | 1 900 | 1 000 | 1 300 | 4 200 |

Despite the existence of relatively clear definitions of salinity, country estimates show wide ranges of values (Table 14A and 14B). It should be noted that some of these include naturally occurring saline soils. For *India*, all are higher than the GLASOD value of 4 M ha, ranging between 7 and 26 M ha. For *Pakistan*, there is better agreement; leaving aside three estimates of 9-16 M ha, the GLASOD and six country estimates lie in the range 4-8 M ha. Two apparently independent surveys, by the Soil Survey of Pakistan and the Water and Power Development Authority, show relative agreement at 5.3 and 4.2 M ha respectively.

Some of the large areas mapped for *Iran* consist in part of soils may have been naturally saline to some degree. Some also became salinized at earlier periods, before the modern era; there are records of people living in areas which are now unpopulated due to saline soils (A. Farshad, personal communication). Since the present report is concerned with the modern era, the GLASOD estimate of area of salinization has been reduced.

In *Bangladesh*, an extension inland of coastal soil salinity has been noted in recent years, where the reduced river flows, consequent upon irrigation, is not sufficient to dilute and displace sea water. In *Sri Lanka*, small areas of light salinization have appeared on irrigated lands of the Mahaweli scheme; the problem has not yet reached serious proportions, but should be monitored.

Estimates of the extent of saline soils need to be associated with the dates of survey. Through successful reclamation, the extent of saline soils has been reduced in some areas, particularly as a consequence of the series of Salinity Control and Reclamation Projects (SCARP) in Pakistan. For example in the Pakistan Punjab the area of waterlogged and saline soils, which had risen from 61 000 ha in 1960 to 68 000 in 1966, had been reduced to 23 000 ha by 1985 (Chopra, 1989).

On the basis of this information, **the GLASOD estimates for India, Iran and Pakistan are revised as in Table 14C.**

## LOWERING OF THE WATER TABLE (Table 15, Figure 6)

In areas of deep alluvial deposits and where the groundwater has not become saline, tubewell irrigation has become widespread, and has led to substantial increases in crop production. Its very success has, however, led to over-extraction of water, in excess of the rates of recharge. A consequence is that the groundwater table has been progressively lowered.

TABLE 15
**GLASOD assessment: areas affected by lowering of the groundwater table**

Unit: 1000 ha

|  | Light | Moderate | Strong | Total | Total as percent of agricultural land |
|---|---|---|---|---|---|
| Afghanistan | 0 | 0 | 0 | 0 | 0% |
| Bangladesh | 0 | 0 | 0 | 0 | 0% |
| Bhutan | 0 | 0 | 0 | 0 | 0% |
| India | 0 | 0 | 0 | 0 | 0% |
| Iran | 12 067 | 7 434 | 0 | 19 502 | 33% |
| Nepal | 0 | 0 | 0 | 0 | 0% |
| Pakistan | 0 | 121 | 0 | 121 | 0.5% |
| Sri Lanka | 0 | 0 | 0 | 0 | 0% |
| India, dry region | 0 | 0 | 0 | 0 | - |
| India, humid region | 0 | 0 | 0 | 0 | - |
| Dry zone | 12 067 | 7 555 | 0 | 19 622 | 13% |
| Humid zone | 0 | 0 | 0 | 0 | 0% |
| Region | 12 067 | 7 555 | 0 | 19 622 | 6% |

In the GLASOD estimate, nearly all of the 20 M ha reported are in Iran, where there is much irrigation from wells and abstraction beyond the capacity for recharge is widespread. An area of 0.1 M ha is reported for Pakistan. The absence of a reported area for India suggests that lowering of the water table was not recognized by the responding organization as a form of 'land' degradation.

This form of degradation has certainly occurred in India. In parts of the Punjab, the water table has fallen by between 0.5 and 4.0 m in the eight year period 1978-86, and is receding at 0.3-0.5 m per year (Singh, 1992). In the Sudhar block of Ludhiana district, it has fallen between 1965 and 1989 from 3 m to 11 m, and in Haryana between 1974 and 1989 from 4.8 m to 7.7 m (Joshi and Tyagi, 1991).

Data on the extent of such lowering in India have not been identified, and the definitions of degrees of severity are not fully applicable to this type of degradation. However, on the basis of these reports, nominal additions to the GLASOD estimates of 100 000 ha light and 100 000 ha moderate degradation are made.

## OTHER TYPES OF DEGRADATION

### Deforestation and forest degradation

Deforestation is a widespread and serious type of land degradation in the region. At the same time, it is a major cause of other types of degradation, particularly water and wind erosion.

The extent of forest cover in 1980 and 1990, and the annual rate of deforestation, is the subject of a current FAO project, *Forest resources assessment 1990*. As the most reliable recent estimate, the data given by this project are adopted in the present study. It should be

TABLE 16
**Estimates of forest are and rate of deforestation**

| Country | Total land area (M ha) | Forest area 1980 (M ha) | Forest area 1990 (M ha) | Forest cover 1990 (%) | Annual Deforestation (1000 ha) | Rate of Change (%) |
|---|---|---|---|---|---|---|
| Bangladesh | 13.0 | 1.1 | 0.8 | 5.9 | 38 | -3.28 |
| Bhutan | 4.7 | 3.0 | 2.8 | 59.8 | 16 | -0.55 |
| India | 297.3 | 55.1 | 51.7 | 17.4 | 339 | -0.62 |
| Nepal | 13.7 | 5.6 | 5.0 | 36.7 | 54 | -0.98 |
| Pakistan | 77.1 | 2.6 | 1.9 | 2.4 | 77 | -2.92 |
| Sri Lanka | 6.5 | 2.0 | 1.7 | 7.0 | 27 | -1.34 |
| Total, 6 countries | 412.3 | 69.4 | 63.9 | 15.5 | 551 | -0.79 |

Data for Afghanistan and Iran are not currently available.

Source:  FAO forest resources assessment 1990 project.

noted, however, that like the estimates for other forms of degradation, these data are by no means fully agreed. Other estimates exist both for total forest area and rate of deforestation, which differ by as much as 50% in some cases.

The FAO data are shown in Table 16. In absolute terms, the annual rate of deforestation has been highest for India, at 339 000 ha per year, whilst clearance rates of over 50 000 ha per year occur in Nepal and Pakistan. Even the small country of Bhutan has been losing 16 000 ha of forest each year. In instances these clearances are reducing what are already very small total forest areas, under 6% of the country for Bangladesh and under 3 percent for Pakistan. Both these countries are losing 3% of their small remaining forest areas annually.

Quantitative data from the FAO assessment are not currently available for Afghanistan and Iran, but rates of deforestation there are known to be high. Further information on deforestation for countries of the region is given in ESCAP (1986).

A related form of land degradation is **forest degradation**, the reduction of the standing biomass and, in extreme cases, potential for regrowth of areas which still remain as forest or woodland (Banerjee and Grimes, in press). Forest degradation results from the cutting of woody formations in excess of their capacity for regrowth. Most involve cutting of natural forests, but illegal clearances of forest plantations are also found. The problem is particularly serious, for example, in Nepal and Pakistan, but occurs widely in the region.

**Rangeland degradation**

*Rangeland degradation* is reduction in the capacity of natural rangelands to support livestock. It occurs as a result of excessive livestock populations, inadequate pasture management, or both.

It has not been possible to obtain quantitative estimates of the extent and severity of rangeland degradation, although these may exist in some of the grassland research institutes of countries of the region. There is no doubt, however, that the problem is widespread in all countries of the dry zone.

In *Pakistan*, the productivity of most of the large area of rangelands is estimated to be 10-50% of its potential (Asian Development Bank, 1992a); however, there may still be the capacity for quite rapid recovery where appropriate pasture management measures are taken (N. Martin, personal communication). In *India*, with some 200 M cattle, grazing pressures have caused widespread exhaustion of the stored food reserves of perennial grasses and their replacement by coarse grasses (Singh, 1988). Rangeland degradation is reported to be severe and widespread in *Afghanistan* (ESCAP, 1983).

As defined above, **desertification** refers to all types of land degradation in the dry zone of the region. It is therefore not separately assessed. Accounts, with some quantitative data, are given in reports of the Desertification Control Network for Asia and the Pacific (DESCONAP) (ESCAP, 1983, 1987, 1991b) and in country reports for Iran (Kholdebarin, 1992; Noohi, 1992) and Pakistan (Hutchinson and Webb, 1987). Desertification, described as the transformation of savanna to steppe and desert, is reported to have affected large areas of India (Singh, 1988). It is also widespread and serious in Afghanistan, Iran and Pakistan.

## WATERSHED DEGRADATION AND MANAGEMENT

In mountain and hill regions, land development is frequently and appropriately conducted in terms of watershed management planning. It is correspondingly possible to assess land degradation on a watershed basis, classifying watersheds on a range from non-degraded to severely degraded, as a basis for selecting priority areas for action. An estimate of this kind has been made, for example, for 100 watersheds in Nepal (FAO, 1988, p.9). Watershed degradation comprises elements of:

▫  deforestation;
▫  soil erosion (water and/or wind);
▫  adverse changes to river flow regime and sediment content.

Data obtained from watershed surveys have been included in the above estimates of degradation. The watershed is a suitable basis for planning the control of land degradation in upland areas, particularly steeply sloping lands. Questions of watershed management are discussed in a number of reports for the Asian region (FAO, 1986a, 1988; FAO/RAPA, 1986; Doolette and Magrath, 1990; Magrath and Doolette, 1990; Castro, 1991).

## SUMMARY: THE SEVERITY AND EXTENT OF LAND DEGRADATION

Table 17 and Figure 8 show total degradation according to the GLASOD data. This table and map exclude double counting, that is, areas affected by more than one kind of degradation are included only once in the totals. A total of 43% of the agricultural land of the region is assessed as affected by some type and degree of degradation. A higher proportion of the dry zone is affected than the humid zone. Most areas of non-degraded land occur either in rainfed lands of the humid zone or irrigated alluvial areas of both zones. All countries except Bhutan are assessed as having over 25% of agricultural land degraded.

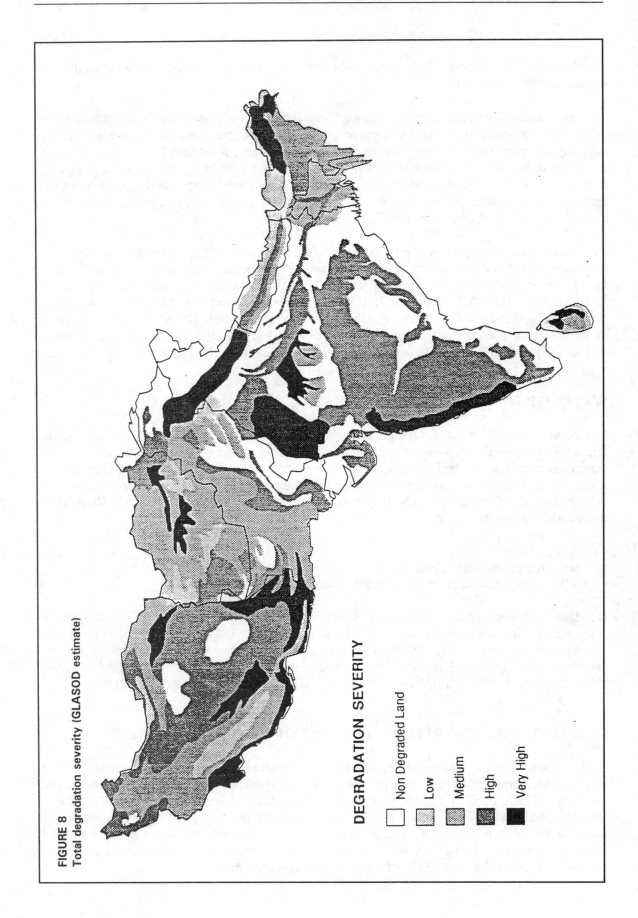

**FIGURE 8**
**Total degradation severity (GLASOD estimate)**

**DEGRADATION SEVERITY**

☐ Non Degraded Land

▨ Low

▨ Medium

▨ High

■ Very High

TABLE 17
**GLASOD assessment: total areas by degree of degradation**

Unit: 1000 ha

|  | Light | Moderate | Strong | Total | Total as percent of agricultural land |
|---|---|---|---|---|---|
| Afghanistan | 9 811 | 2 597 | 209 | 12 617 | 33% |
| Bangladesh | 6 187 | 1 080 | 0 | 7 267 | 75% |
| Bhutan | 36 | 0 | 4 | 40 | 10% |
| India | 2 935 | 20 128 | 21 941 | 45 005 | 25% |
| Iran | 17 721 | 29 574 | 8 301 | 55 596 | 94% |
| Nepal | 429 | 759 | 0 | 1 188 | 26% |
| Pakistan | 7 530 | 8 243 | 0 | 15 773 | 61% |
| Sri Lanka | 35 | 158 | 838 | 1 030 | 44% |
| India, dry region | 1 176 | 3 083 | 10 899 | 15 158 | - |
| India, humid region | 1 759 | 17 045 | 11 042 | 29 846 | - |
| Dry zone | 36 238 | 43 497 | 19 409 | 99 144 | 66% |
| Humid zone | 9 338 | 19 042 | 11 883 | 40 263 | 24% |
| Region | 45 576 | 62 538 | 31 293 | 139 408 | 43% |

Note:    For areas with more than one type of degradation the most severe type is used for summation.

Table 18 and 19 show the best estimates from the present study, based initially upon GLASOD data but modified for certain types of degradation and particular countries as given above. The totals include 'double counting', i.e. areas affected by more than one type of degradation. Water erosion is the most widespread form of degradation, affecting both humid and dry zones. Nearly 40% of the dry zone is affected by wind erosion. Soil fertility decline is certainly widespread, but its extent is not know quantitatively; the values shown are tentative estimates, and may be lower or higher. Waterlogging, salinization and lowering of the water table are of smaller total extent, but their effect is proportionally more serious in that they affect mainly irrigated lands, which when undegraded have high productive potential.

Areas with the most severe and extensive land degradation include:

◻    the cultivated Himalayan mountain belt stretching through northern India and Nepal (water erosion);
◻    the Western Ghats of the Indian Deccan (water erosion);
◻    highland watershed areas of Sri Lanka (water erosion);
◻    semi-desert areas of Iran, Afghanistan, and the Thar desert of India (wind erosion and salinization);
◻    areas of irrigated land on the Indo-Gangetic plains of Pakistan and India (salinization).

These are among the priority areas for action to prevent further degradation. In addition, however, evidence suggests that the problem of soil fertility decline is more widespread, at least to the degree defined as light, and is of increasing severity; besides the large areas of Bangladesh and Sri Lanka given by the GLASOD survey, the problem affects substantial areas of both India and Pakistan.

TABLE 18
**Best estimates of areas affected by land degradation**

Unit: 1000 ha

| | Light | Moderate | Strong | Total | Total as percent of agricultural land |
|---|---|---|---|---|---|
| **WATER EROSION** | | | | | |
| Afghanistan | 8.6 | 2.6 | 0.0 | 11.2 | 29% |
| Bangladesh | 0.0 | 1.5 | 0.0 | 1.5 | 15% |
| Bhutan | <0.1 | 0.0 | <0.1 | <0.1 | 10% |
| India* | 2.9 | 17.2 | 12.6 | 32.8 | 18% |
| Iran | 14.5 | 11.9 | 0.0 | 26.4 | 45% |
| Nepal | 0.5 | 1.1 | 0.0 | 1.6 | 34% |
| Pakistan | 6.1 | 1.1 | 0.0 | 7.2 | 28% |
| Sri Lanka | 0.1 | 0.2 | 0.8 | 1.1 | 46% |
| India, dry region | 1.2 | 0.0 | 1.7 | 2.9 | - |
| India, humid region | 1.8 | 17.2 | 10.9 | 29.9 | - |
| Region | 32.7 | 35.6 | 13.5 | 81.7 | 25% |
| **WIND EROSION** | | | | | |
| Afghanistan | 1.9 | 0.0 | 0.2 | 2.1 | 5% |
| Bangladesh | 0.0 | 0.0 | 0.0 | 0.0 | 0% |
| Bhutan | 0.0 | 0.0 | 0.0 | 0.0 | 0% |
| India | 0.0 | 1.8 | 9.0 | 10.8 | 6% |
| Iran | 6.6 | 25.7 | 3.1 | 35.4 | 60% |
| Nepal | 0.0 | 0.0 | 0.0 | 0.0 | 0% |
| Pakistan | 4.0 | 6.7 | 0.0 | 10.7 | 42% |
| Sri Lanka | 0.0 | 0.0 | 0.0 | 0.0 | 0% |
| India, dry region | 0.0 | 1.8 | 9.0 | 10.8 | - |
| India, humid region | 0.0 | 0.0 | 0.0 | 0.0 | - |
| Dry zone | 12.4 | 34.2 | 12.3 | 59.0 | 39% |
| Humid zone | 0.0 | 0.0 | 0.0 | 0.0 | 0% |
| Region | 12.4 | 34.2 | 12.3 | 59.0 | 18% |
| **SOIL FERTILITY DECLINE** | | | | | |
| Afghanistan | 0.0 | 0.0 | 0.0 | 0.0 | 0% |
| Bangladesh | 6.4 | 0.0 | 0.0 | 6.4 | 65% |
| Bhutan | 0.0 | 0.0 | 0.0 | 0.0 | 0% |
| India | 26.2 | 0.0 | 3.2 | 29.4 | 16% |
| Iran | 0.0 | 0.0 | 0.0 | 0.0 | 0% |
| Nepal | 0.0 | 0.0 | 0.0 | 0.0 | 0% |
| Pakistan | 5.2 | 0.0 | 0.0 | 5.2 | 20% |
| Sri Lanka | 0.7 | 0.7 | 0.0 | 1.4 | 61% |
| India, dry region | 2.2 | 0.0 | 0.0 | 2.2 | - |
| India, humid region | 24.0 | 0.0 | 3.2 | 27.2 | - |
| Dry zone | 7.4 | 0.0 | 0.0 | 7.4 | 5% |
| Humid zone | 31.1 | 0.7 | 3.2 | 35.0 | 20% |
| Region | 38.5 | 0.7 | 3.2 | 42.4 | 13% |

| | Light | Moderate | Strong | Total | Total as percent of agricultural land |
|---|---|---|---|---|---|
| **WATERLOGGING** | | | | | |
| Afghanistan | 0.0 | 0.0 | 0.0 | 0.0 | 0% |
| Bangladesh | 0.0 | 0.0 | 0.0 | 0.0 | 0% |
| Bhutan | 0.0 | 0.0 | 0.0 | 0.0 | 0% |
| India | 0.0 | 3.1 | 0.0 | 3.1 | 2% |
| Iran | 0.5 | 0.0 | 0.0 | 0.5 | 1% |
| Nepal | 0.0 | 0.0 | 0.0 | 0.0 | 0% |
| Pakistan | 0.8 | 0.4 | 0.8 | 2.0 | 8% |
| Sri Lanka | 0.0 | 0.0 | 0.0 | 0.0 | 0% |
| India, dry region | 0.0 | 3.1 | 0.0 | 3.1 | - |
| India, humid region | 0.0 | 0.0 | 0.0 | 0.0 | - |
| Dry zone | 1.4 | 3.5 | 0.8 | 5.7 | 4% |
| Humid zone | 0.0 | 0.0 | 0.0 | 0.0 | 0% |
| Region | 1.4 | 3.5 | 0.8 | 5.7 | 2% |
| **SALINIZATION** | | | | | |
| Afghanistan | 1.3 | 0.0 | 0.0 | 1.3 | 3% |
| Bangladesh | 0.0 | 0.0 | 0.0 | 0.0 | 0% |
| Bhutan | 0.0 | 0.0 | 0.0 | 0.0 | 0% |
| India | 0.0 | 3.5 | 3.5 | 7.0 | 4% |
| Iran | 5.0 | 7.0 | 4.0 | 16.0 | 27% |
| Nepal | 0.0 | 0.0 | 0.0 | 0.0 | 0% |
| Pakistan | 1.9 | 1.0 | 1.3 | 4.2 | 16% |
| Sri Lanka | <0.1 | 0.0 | 0.0 | <0.1 | 2% |
| India, dry region | 0.0 | 3.5 | 3.5 | 7.0 | - |
| India, humid region | 0.0 | 0.0 | 0.3 | 0.3 | - |
| Dry zone | 8.2 | 11.5 | 8.5 | 28.1 | 19% |
| Humid zone | <0.1 | <0.1 | 0.3 | 0.4 | <1% |
| Region | 8.2 | 11.5 | 38.8 | 28.5 | 9% |
| **LOWERING OF THE WATER TABLE** | | | | | |
| Afghanistan | 0.0 | 0.0 | 0.0 | 0.0 | 0% |
| Bangladesh | 0.0 | 0.0 | 0.0 | 0.0 | 0% |
| Bhutan | 0.0 | 0.0 | 0.0 | 0.0 | 0% |
| India | 0.1 | 0.1 | 0.0 | 0.2 | <1% |
| Iran | 12.1 | 7.4 | 0.0 | 19.5 | 33% |
| Nepal | 0.0 | 0.0 | 0.0 | 0.0 | 0% |
| Pakistan | 0.0 | 0.1 | 0.0 | 0.1 | <1% |
| Sri Lanka | 0.0 | 0.0 | 0.0 | 0.0 | 0% |
| India, dry region | 0.1 | 0.1 | 0.0 | 0.2 | - |
| India, humid region | 0.0 | 0.0 | 0.0 | 0.0 | - |
| Dry zone | 12.2 | 7.7 | 0.0 | 19.8 | 13% |
| Humid zone | 0.0 | 0.0 | 0.0 | 0.0 | 0% |
| Region | 12.2 | 7.7 | 0.0 | 19.8 | 6% |

\*    Values of water erosion for India may be substantially higher.

TABLE 19
**Percentages of agricultural land affected by degradation: summary**

| Type of land degradation | Percent of agricultural land affected | | |
|---|---|---|---|
| | Dry zone | Humid zone | Region |
| Water erosion | 32 | 20 | 25 |
| Wind erosion | 39 | 0 | 18 |
| Soil fertility decline | 5 | 20 | 13 |
| Waterlogging | 4 | 0 | 2 |
| Salinization | 19 | <1 | 9 |
| Lowering of the water table | 13 | 0 | 6 |

## DISCUSSION

The wide range of estimates for the nature and extent of many types of land degradation has been repeatedly noted. Estimates frequently differ by as much as 100%, in some cases more. Reasons for this variation are:

1.  Failure to define sufficiently precisely the degree of degradation that is being assessed, and thus to define working rules for surveying its severity in the field.

2.  The absence, over most areas, of reliable surveys of degradation.

3.  The repeated copying of estimates from one source to another, which can give a specious appearance of authority, whilst making it difficult to trace the original source and its basis.

Two recommendations arise from this. First, further efforts should be made to define degrees of severity of land degradation; these should be in terms that permit objective surveys and monitoring. Secondly, field surveys of existing soil degradation and, most importantly, monitoring of soil changes, should be conducted, in order to improve the state of knowledge.

This overall situation raises an important question: should greater efforts, including investment, immediately be made to combat land degradation, or should these await the acquisition of better data? A 'contrary' view exists, which may be expressed as follows:

> "Estimates of the extent of land degradation, and/or of their effects on production, may be considerably exaggerated. They may have been magnified by sectional interests in conservation, or by governments. Because the data are so uncertain, we do not know whether degradation is as serious as it is claimed to be. Unless and until there is a better foundation of evidence, we cannot justify the expenditure of scarce development funds on measures to combat degradation."

This view serves one important purpose, in that it places emphasis on what are, indeed, large uncertainties in estimates of the extent of degradation and its effects.

Whilst it is certainly true that some of the estimates are based on questionable foundations, this view is rejected. Reports from all countries of the region (supported for sample areas by the authors of this study) point to the certain existence of two types of situation:

1.  Severe degradation in certain areas; e.g. gullying, total removal of topsoil by sheet erosion, complete salinization.

2.  Light to moderate degradation over extensive areas; e.g. the evidence for soil fertility decline and reduced productivity of rangelands.

**It is therefore concluded that, although more precise data should be obtained, the total evidence is sufficient to call for immediate action to prevent further land degradation and, where still possible, to reverse the effects of past degradation.**

# Chapter 6

# Causes of land degradation

The causes of land degradation can be divided into natural hazards, direct causes, and underlying causes. *Natural hazards* are the conditions of the physical environment which lead to the existence of a high degradation hazard, for example steep slopes as a hazard for water erosion. *Direct causes* are unsuitable land use and inappropriate land management practices, for example the cultivation of steep slopes without measures for soil conservation. *Underlying causes* are the reasons why these inappropriate types of land use and management are practised; for example, the slopes may be cultivated because the landless poor need food, and conservation measures not adopted because these farmers lack security of tenure.

There is a distinction, although with overlap, between unsuitable land use and inappropriate land management practices.

Unsuitable land use is the use of land for purposes for which it is environmentally unsuited for sustainable use. An example is forest clearance and arable use of steeply sloping upper watershed areas which would have more value to the community as water sources, managed under a protective forest cover.

Inappropriate land management practices refer to the use of land in ways which could be sustainable if properly managed, but where the necessary practices are not adopted. An example is the failure to adopt soil conservation measures where these are needed. It can also refer to land use which is ecologically sustainable under low intensity of use but in which the management becomes inappropriate at higher intensities. Examples are shifting cultivation and the grazing of semi-arid rangelands.

The GLASOD assessment gives one or two causes for each map unit and type of degradation. In this assessment, only four causes were recognized, defined as:

◻  deforestation and removal of natural vegetation;
◻  overgrazing;
◻  agricultural activities;
◻  over-exploitation of vegetation for domestic use.

This survey did not recognize a separate class of problems arising in the planning and management of irrigation, but it is clear from the results that such problems are included under agricultural activities.

The results from the GLASOD assessment of causes is summarized in Table 20. Other information on causes is from publications and personal information.

TABLE 20
**Causes of degradation as given in the GLASOD assessment**

| Type of degradation | Percentage area of degradation type caused by | | | |
|---|---|---|---|---|
| | Deforestation | Overgrazing | Agricultural activities | Overcutting of vegetation |
| Water erosion | 61 | 67 | 2 | 44 |
| Wind erosion | 21 | 46 | 1 | 98 |
| Soil fertility decline | 25 | 0 | 75 | 0 |
| Salinization | 34 | 30 | 14 | 87 |
| Waterlogging | 0 | 0 | 85 | 33 |
| Lowering of water table | 12 | 22 | 65 | 34 |
| All types of degradation | 37 | 46 | 15 | 63 |

NB: Up to two causes are given for each type of degradation, therefore percentages sum to more than 100.

## NATURAL DEGRADATION HAZARDS

The major natural hazards in the region, environmental conditions which act as predisposing factors for land degradation, are:

For water erosion:

- monsoonal rains of high intensity;
- steep slopes of the mountain and hill lands;
- soils with low resistance to water erosion (e.g. silty soils, vertisols).

For wind erosion:

- semi-arid to arid climates;
- high rainfall variability, with liability to drought spells;
- soils with low resistance to wind erosion (e.g. sandy soils).
- an open cover of natural vegetation.

For soil fertility decline:

- strong leaching in humid climates;
- soils which are strongly acid, and/or with low natural fertility.

For waterlogging:

- alluvial plains or interior basins which restrict outward drainage of groundwater.

For salinization:

- semi-arid to arid climates with low leaching intensity;

- plains and interior basins which restrict outward drainage of groundwater;
- soils which are naturally slightly saline.

For lowering of the water table:

- semi-arid to arid climates with low rates of groundwater recharge.

In some cases, these natural hazards are of sufficient intensity to give rise to unproductive land without human interference. Examples are the naturally saline soils which occur in some interior basins of dry regions, or areas of natural gullying ('badlands'). Such conditions have been referred to as *problem soils*. Percentages of land covered by problem soils are given in Dent (1990).

With respect to land degradation, the key feature is that land shortage in the region has led to the widespread agricultural use of areas with natural hazards. These are the passive, or predisposing, conditions for land degradation. Problem soils require special care in management, and failure to give such care leads to land degradation.

## DIRECT CAUSES OF DEGRADATION

**Deforestation of unsuitable land** Deforestation is both a type of degradation as such, and also a cause of other types, principally water erosion. Deforestation in itself is not necessarily degrading - without it, most productive agricultural lands (in the temperate zone as well as the tropics) would not be available. Deforestation becomes a cause of degradation first, when the land that is cleared is steeply sloping, or has shallow or easily erodible soils; and secondly, where the clearance is not followed by good management.

The extent of deforestation considered as a type of degradation has been summarized in Chapter 5, Section *Deforestation and forest degradation*. It is the leading cause of water erosion in steeply sloping humid environments. It is also a contributory cause of wind erosion, soil fertility decline and salinization.

**Overcutting of vegetation** Rural people cut natural forests, woodlands and shrublands to obtain timber, fuelwood and other forest products. Such cutting becomes unsustainable where it exceeds the rate of natural regrowth. This has happened widely in semi-arid environments, where fuelwood shortages are often severe. Impoverishment of the natural woody cover of trees and shrubs is a major factor in causing both water erosion and wind erosion. In the GLASOD assessment it is cited as a cause for 98% of the area affected by wind erosion. This assessment also cites it as a contributory cause to salinization.

**Shifting cultivation without adequate fallow periods** In the past, shifting cultivation was a sustainable form of land use, at a time when low population densities allowed forest fallow periods of sufficient length to restore soil properties. Population increase and enforced shortening of fallow periods has led to it becoming non-sustainable. Shifting cultivation is found in the hill areas of north-east India, where it is a cause of water erosion and soil fertility decline.

**Overgrazing** Overgrazing is the grazing of natural pastures at stocking intensities above the livestock carrying capacity. It leads directly to decreases in the quantity and quality of the vegetation cover. This is a leading cause not only of wind erosion, but also of water erosion in dry lands. Both degradation of the vegetation cover and erosion lead to a decline in soil organic matter and physical properties, and hence in resistance to erosion.

Intense grazing at the end of the annual dry season, and during periods of drought, does not necessarily lead to degradation; the vegetation may recover during the succeeding rains. Degradation occurs when the recovery of vegetation and soil properties during periods of normal rainfall does not reach its previous status.

**Non-adoption of soil-conservation management practices** Under arable use, management practices are needed to check water erosion on all sloping lands. In dry lands, measures to check wind erosion are necessary also on level land. Soil conserving management practices may be grouped into:

1.  Biological methods: maintenance of a ground surface cover, of living plants or plant litter; vegetative barriers, including both contour hedgerows and grass strips; and windbreaks and shelterbelts.
2.  Earth structures: terraces, and the various forms of bank-and-ditch structures (bunds, storm drains, etc.).
3.  Maintaining soil resistance to erosion: primarily, maintenance of soil organic matter and thereby aggregation and structure.

Great efforts have been made by soil conservation services in the countries of the region to promote the adoption of such management practices. In some areas, these efforts have achieved a considerable measure of success. In others, staff and resources have been greatly deficient, or adoption of recommended methods poor. The recent change of emphasis in soil conservation with more use of biological methods, including agroforestry, and greater stress on farmers' participation and economic incentives, has not yet been fully taken up by extension services.

Often, it is not the environment nor the type of land use which necessarily leads to degradation, but the standard of management. A clear example is seen in tea production in the hill lands of Sri Lanka. Well-managed farms maintain a complete vegetation cover, which checks erosion even on steep slopes; on poorly-managed farms, rainfall strikes bare soil between plants, leading in places to very severe degradation.

**Extension of cultivation onto lands of lower potential and/or high natural hazards** These are also called 'fragile' or marginal lands. Historically the more fertile, or high-potential, agricultural lands were the first to be occupied. Population increase has led to the widespread use of lands of lower potential, those which are less fertile or have greater degradation hazards. Such marginal lands include:

□   steeply sloping land;
□   areas of shallow or sandy soils, or with laterite crusts;
□   cultivation of semi-arid lands, and grazing of the drier semi-arid areas, marginal to deserts.

Such land is of great extent in the region, and makes a large contribution to its agricultural production. Except in areas of highest environmental hazards, e.g. upper watersheds, it is neither desirable nor practicable that they should be taken out of production. What must be recognized is that such lands require higher standards of management if their resources are to be conserved. Unfortunately, they are often utilized by poorer farmers.

**Improper crop rotations**  As a result of population growth, land shortage and economic pressures, farmers in some areas have adopted cereal-based, intensive crop rotations, based particularly on rice and wheat, in place of the more balanced cereal-legume rotations that were formerly found. This is a contributory cause of soil fertility decline.

**Unbalanced fertilizer use**  Where soil fertility has declined, as a result of prolonged cultivation or erosion, farmers attempt to maintain crop yields. The primary method available for doing so is application of fertilizer. In the short term, a yield response is most readily and cheaply obtained from nitrogenous fertilizer. There has been a steady increase in the ratios of nitrogen to phosphorus, and nitrogen to all other nutrients, in the region. Where phosphate deficiencies have been recognized and counteracted by phosphatic fertilizer, deficiencies of other nutrients, including sulphur and zinc, have been reported.

The short-term measure of combatting fertility decline by application only of macronutrients, and particularly nitrogenous fertilizer, is leading to a greater problem of nutrient imbalance in the medium term. Among the consequences is likely to be lower yield responses to fertilizers.

**Problems arising from planning and management of canal irrigation**  The development of salinization and waterlogging on the large-scale canal irrigation schemes of the Indo-Gangetic plains has been frequently described. Application of water in excess of natural rainfall led to a progressive rise in the water table from the 1930s onward. Where the water table has reached close to the surface, waterlogging occurs leading, through evaporation of water containing salts, to salinization. Sodification follows where sodium replaces other bases in the soil exchange complex. The problem could have been avoided, or reduced, if deep drains had been included in the initial implementation of irrigation schemes. More detailed accounts of the complex processes involved will be found in development planning studies of Pakistan and Indian irrigated areas.

**Overpumping of groundwater**  In areas of non-saline ('sweet') groundwater, the technology of tubewells has led to abstraction of water in excess of natural recharge by rainfall and river seepage. This has progressively lowered the water table, as in Iran, India and Pakistan.

## UNDERLYING CAUSES OF DEGRADATION

There are more basic reasons underlying the reasons for land degradation outlined above. They apply to all direct causes, other than the problems of large-scale irrigation schemes which arose from lack of foresight in planning and management.

**Land shortage** It has always been recognized that land is a finite resource, but only recently has the full impact of this fact occurred. In earlier times, food shortage or poverty could be combatted by taking new, unused, land into cultivation. Over most of South Asia, this solution is no longer available. The percentage change in agricultural land over the ten years 1980-1990 is under 2.5% for India, Pakistan, Sri Lanka and Afghanistan, whilst for Bangladesh there has been a small absolute decrease. The increase recorded for Nepal has certainly been obtained by deforestation and taking into agricultural use sloping land which is difficult to farm on a sustainable basis.

When combined with increases in rural population, land shortage has led to decreases in the already small areas of agricultural land per person in six of the eight countries, including all in the humid zone. The relative decrease in land per person over 1980-90 was 14% for India and 22% for Pakistan. In Iran, with a smaller rural population increase, the land/people ratio has remained virtually constant.

There is almost no unused but usable land in South Asia. All of the best land is already taken up, and that which is not, cannot be used agriculturally on a sustainable basis.

**Land tenure: tenancy and open access resources** Farmers will be reluctant to invest in measures to conserve land resources if their future rights to use these resources are not secure. Two kinds of property rights lead to this situation, tenancy and open access resources.

Despite efforts by legislation and land reform programmes over many years, tenant occupation of farmland is still very widespread. The landowner is now frequently from the cities, and the land is farmed by tenants paying some form of rental. Relations between landlord and tenant are often good, and the tenant in fact remains on the same farm for many years. However, such tenants lack the incentive to maintain the land in good condition, being interested mainly in the immediate harvest.

Open access land resources are those which anyone, in practice the poor and otherwise landless, can use, without rights of continuing usufruct or tenure. This applies mainly to forest lands, nominally under government ownership but which are settled on a squatter basis.

There is a distinction between common property and open access resources. In common property resources, use is restricted to members of a community, village or clan, and is subject to constraints, socially applied. For example, pastoralists often have customs for when certain areas must be rested from grazing, villages restrict the cutting of communal woodland. On open access land there are no such constraints. With no legal basis to their use, incentive to farm the land other than for immediate needs is completely lacking. This is a serious cause of deforestation followed by water erosion.

**Economic pressures and attitudes** Small land holdings lead to severe economic pressures on farmers, to obtain sufficient food and income to meet immediate needs. Because of such pressure in the short term, labour, land and capital resources cannot be spared to care for the land, for example green manuring or soil conservation structures. This is also the underlying reason for two other direct causes noted above, improper crop rotations and unbalanced fertilizer use.

A contributory factor, not always appreciated by outside observers, is a change in economic attitudes. In former times, most farmers accepted the situation into which they were born, even if it was one of relative poverty. Modern communications and influence have led to greater aspirations and consequent requirements for income, thus increasing economic pressures.

**Poverty** Countries of the region have made great progress in economic development, achieving increases in gross domestic product per capita. It is questionable whether there have been corresponding improvements in the real welfare of the rural poor. The majority of farmers remain close to, or below, the margin of poverty, defined as access to basic necessities of life.

Poverty leads to land degradation. It could almost certainly be shown that richer farmers maintain their soils in better state than poorer. Research based on sample studies to confirm this is desirable.

**Population increase** Together with land shortage, the second basic cause of degradation is the continuing increase in rural, agricultural, population. Growth rates for total population 1980-1990 for six countries range from 2.1-3.6% per year (for Afghanistan the figure is affected by migration and war). Only in Sri Lanka have attempts to reduce the rate of population increase made substantial progress, with a growth rate of 1.4%.

Urban populations are increasing faster than rural. The trend towards urbanization, however, is not sufficient to reverse the key that *absolute levels of rural population have increased and are increasing*. In Bangladesh, Bhutan, India, Nepal and Pakistan, rural populations were 17-32% higher in 1990 than in 1980. In absolute terms, the scale is greatest in India, where already densely populated rural areas contained 79 million more people in 1990 than 10 years earlier.

## LAND, POPULATION, POVERTY AND DEGRADATION: THE CAUSAL NEXUS

The direct and indirect causes of degradation are linked by a chain of cause and effect, or causal nexus (Figure 9).

The two external, or driving, forces are *limited land resources* and *increase in rural population*. Expressed another way, there are no longer substantial areas of usable, unused land in the region; but the number of people to be supported from this finite land resource is increasing every year.

These two primary forces combine to produce *land shortage*. This refers to increasing pressure of population on land, resulting in small farms, low production per person and increasing landlessness. A consequence of land shortage is the next element, *poverty*.

Land shortage and poverty, taken together, lead to *non-sustainable land management practices*, meaning the direct causes of degradation. For reasons outlined above, poor farmers are led to clear forest, cultivate steep slopes without conservation, overgraze rangelands, make unbalanced fertilizer applications, and the other causes noted above.

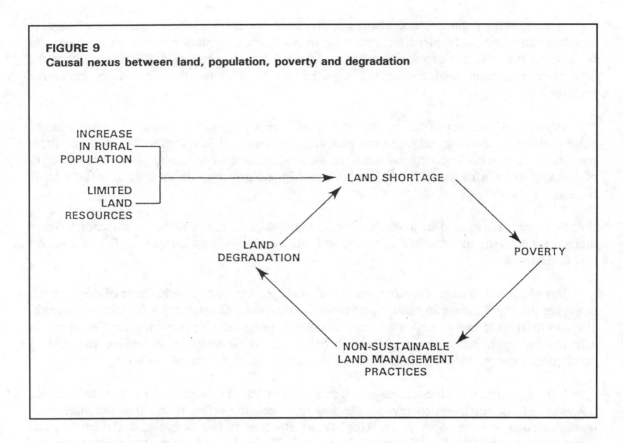

**FIGURE 9**
**Causal nexus between land, population, poverty and degradation**

The non-sustainable management practices lead to *land degradation*. This leads to reduced land productivity: a lower response to the same inputs or, where farmers possess the resources, a need for higher inputs to maintain crop yields and farm incomes. This has the effect of increasing land shortage, thus completing the cycle.

Case studies illustrating the interconnections of this cycle are given in Asian Development Bank (1991).

There are two ways to check this cycle, improved technology and reduction in population increase. Improved technology could be added as a third external force in Figure 1, divided into three elements:

◻  land improvements (e.g. irrigation), which can reduce land shortage;
◻  increases in productive technology, which can reduce  poverty and pressure upon land;
◻  better land resource conservation, which can reduce land degradation and, to a limited degree, reverse degradation.

Vast efforts have been made, by individual farmers, national governments and through international development assistance, to counteract the cycle of poverty and land degradation by research and development of improved technology. Much success has been achieved, as in the spread of high-yielding crop varieties and use of fertilizers which was (optimistically) called the 'green revolution'.

All of this effort will be nullified, and in places reversed, if it is not accompanied by a reduction in rate of growth of population. The existence of limited land resources cannot be substantially changed. The other external force, increase in population, constantly drives the cycle that leads to poverty and land degradation.

Governments of the region, as well as international agencies, recognize the priority of limiting increase in population, as evidenced by reports. There is also the beginning of an awareness that population questions cannot be treated in isolation, but must be linked with sustainable land development. What is significant is that recognition of the nexus is found not just among land resource institutions or Ministries of Agriculture, but widely within Asian development agencies, as illustrated by the following quotations:

"It is population growth working in conjunction with other factors that is bringing about widespread environmental deterioration" (FAO/RAPA, 1990, p.10).

"Population issues currently encompass areas of concern such as poverty alleviation, environmental degradation...which are much broader than population size and growth alone" (ESCAP, 1991a, para. 529).

"Few institutions have developed a response strategy to the implications of population pressure on natural resource management" (Asian Development Bank, 1991, p.21).

"A significant reduction in population growth rates is absolutely essential for visible improvements in human development levels" (Asia Development Bank, 1990, p.48).

"Hypothetical village-level consequences of rapid population growth...1. Environmental degradation: soil erosion/exhaustion, reduced fallow periods, movement to marginal farmlands, deforestation" (ESCAP, 1989, p.90).

Two views from outside the region may be added, from the most recent FAO and World Bank reviews:

"A lack of control over resources; population growth; a lack of alternative avenues of livelihood; and inequity are all contributing to the degradation of the regions's [Asia] resources. **In turn, environmental degradation perpetuates poverty, as the poorest attempt to survive on a diminishing resource base**" (FAO, 1992, p. 106).

"The close link between poverty and environmental problems makes a compelling case for increasing assistance to reduce poverty and [to] slow population growth...Rapid population growth can exacerbate the mutually reinforcing effects of poverty and environmental damage. **The poor are both victims and agents of environmental damage**" (World Bank, 1992, pp. 3 and 7).

Statements recognizing the need to reduce population for the welfare of their people have been made by all governments of the region (e.g. ESCAP, 1987a). In a regional study of natural disasters and protection of the environment, a summary table gives among causes of environmental problems, "population" for five of the six South Asian countries and "poverty" for four countries (SAARC, 1992, pp. 190-197).

Chapter 7

# Economic consequences of land degradation

## INTRODUCTION: ECONOMIC AND SOCIAL CONSEQUENCES

Chapters 7 and 8 are concerned with the economic and social consequences of land degradation: its implications for the community as a whole, and thus for governments, and its effects upon the people, the rural population of the areas affected. One of the main social consequences is, in fact, also an economic one, namely reduced income for the farmers; whilst analysis at the macroeconomic level is ultimately based upon aggregating the effects of degradation upon individual farmers.

This chapter covers the economic consequences of land degradation considered at the national and regional level: its cost to the countries and their people. The effects on the rural population, including reduced incomes, are discussed in Chapter 8.

## ECONOMIC VALUATION OF NATURAL RESOURCES AND DEGRADATION

### Concepts and approaches in natural resource accounting

Natural resource accounting is a relatively new concept. Its implications for land degradation are so great that an introductory outline of the concept and methods is called for.

The basis is simple: that natural resources, such as minerals, soils and forests, have an economic value. This is called *natural capital*, to be distinguished from manufactured capital such as roads, factories and machinery. Changes in manufactured capital - construction and depreciation - have always been considered in both financial and economic analysis. Until recently, changes in natural capital have not been given money values, nor included in cost-benefit and other forms of economic analysis. Changes in natural capital are not currently included in systems of national accounting, although there is pressure for their inclusion.

Natural resources have formerly been priced only in terms of their cost of use: minerals were priced only at the costs of extracting them, forests at the logging costs. In the case of soils, these were treated as the 'land' factor in classical economics, priced at the market value of farmland. In effect, the capital value of the resources themselves was priced as zero. It was assumed that they were so abundant as to have no scarcity value.

This led to some gross distortions in the apparent creation of wealth. Minerals are extracted, or forests cut down, and the money received from their sale is treated as national income. The decrease in the reserves of minerals or area of forest does not appear in the accounts. Wealth appears to have been created, based on the 'free' natural resources.

The example of minerals refers to a non-renewable natural resource, that of forest to a renewable one. The situation for soil and water resources is more complex. The milder forms of land degradation, for example soil nutrient depletion, can be reversed by changes in management; the resource is renewable, and the degradation reversible. In the case of two severe forms of degradation, salinization and waterlogging, land productivity can be restored by reclamation, even where degradation has progressed to the point of total loss of production; the degradation is reversible, although at high costs, as shown by the SCARP projects of Pakistan. Soil degradation may be reversible or irreversible, as discussed below.

In the case of soil erosion, some of the effects may appear to be reversible, through checking further erosion by soil conservation programmes and restoring lost nutrients and organic matter. Where land has been lost by gullying, or severe sheet erosion has removed the soil down to a gravelly residue, degradation is clearly irreversible. It should be noted, however, that this applies also to any actual loss of soil material, or reduced profile depth, since the rate of natural soil formation is extremely slow on a human time scale.

Two recent case studies, in the Philippines and Indonesia, illustrate the orders of magnitude which may be involved. In the Philippines it has been estimated that there is an annual rate of natural resource depletion equivalent to 4% of the gross domestic product (World Bank, 1989; Cruz and Repetto, 1992). For Indonesia, inclusion of the loss of timber, oil and soil resources had the effect of reducing gross domestic produce by about 20%, whilst gross domestic investment was reduced to low, and in one year negative, values. The annual depletion of soil fertility was calculated as 4% of the value of crop production, or as large as the annual increase in production (Repetto *et al.*, 1989; Magrath and Arens, 1989).

Discussions of methods of natural resource accounting, drawn upon as the basis for the present discussion, include Ahmad *et al.*, (1989), Chisholm and Dumsday (1987), Lutz and El Serafy (1988), Pearce and Turner (1990), Peskin (1989), Pezzey (1992) and Southgate (1989). A report of a seminar specific to Asia is given in Sun (1989), and a consideration of natural resource accounting for India by Parikh *et al.* (1992).

## Methods for the valuation of soil resources

Soil resources have been valued chiefly as the basis for analyzing the economics of soil conservation projects (Bojö, 1992; Magrath, 1989). There has also been extensive cost-benefit analysis of reclamation projects to counter salinization and waterlogging. Five methods are found:

1   **Defensive expenditure** This is the cost of preventing the land degradation by soil conservation works, drainage systems on irrigation schemes, and similar preventative measures. These have both capital and recurrent elements of expenditure.

2   **Lost production** This method is widely used, and has the advantage of being applicable to all types of land degradation. Crop yields, or other output, are estimated for the non-degraded and degraded soil, and then priced. The difference measures the value of lost production. The two situations, with and without degradation, are assessed by normal methods of farm economics.

3   **Replacement cost** Of necessity, farmers go to much effort to avoid losses in production. The principal means open to them is to increase fertilizer inputs in order to maintain yields. For

the same yield level, the additional fertilizer needed is a measure of the cost of degradation. This can be treated by estimating the quantity of nitrogen, phosphorus and potassium removed in eroded soil. The cost of degradation is valued at the cost of replacing these nutrients by fertilizer. An estimate on this basis has been made for Zambia (Stocking, 1986).

4　**User cost**　This refers to the proportion of profits which need to be reinvested in some other way, if the same income is to be maintained after the resource has been exhausted (Lutz and El Seraphy, 1988). For example, some of the profits from extracting oil could be invested in construction of wind power generators. Applied to soils, it would mean that a proportion of the profits made from some exploitative, degrading, land use were reinvested in some other way, say in reclaiming coastal marshland.

5　**Restoration or reclamation**　This is the cost of restoring the soil to its former productive state. In the case of salinization and waterlogging practical means are known, such as drainage, leaching and gypsum application, and have been costed. For lowering of the water table, it would refer to the production foregone by not abstracting water until its former level had been restored, but this is not a realistic proposition.

For the case of soil erosion, restoration costs have been incompletely assessed in previous analyses. Suppose that land has lost 5 cm topsoil. It is not sufficient to value the cost of installing soil conservation measures, followed by improved land management, for one is still working with the depleted, shallower, soil. If the soil is to be restored to its former conditions then it is necessary to:

▫　Replace nutrients, as in method 2 above.
▫　Replace soil organic matter, and thereby restore structure; this could be done, for example, by allotting part of the land to a green manure crop, foregoing production.
▫　Replace the soil.

One way to replace lost soil would be to buy it, as can be done from a horticultural supplier. This solution succeeds in putting a market money value on soil volume, but is environmentally unacceptable, since it is robbing one area to restore another. The only true way to restore lost soil is by taking land out of production until it is restored by the natural process of weathering. The rate of this process varies by orders of magnitude for different rock types, but for consolidated strata it has been estimated as a maximum of 500 mm per thousand years (Saunders and Young, 1983). In soil conservation circles a top rate of "one inch in 30-300 years", or about 0.1-1.0 mm per year, has been quoted (Schertz, 1983). Assuming natural erosion to be very slow, then even at the fastest of these rates, it would mean *putting land under fallow for 50 years* to restore the lost 5 cm. This again is unrealistic as a practical proposition, but it gives a measure of the true resource loss incurred.

**Provisional nature of these estimates**

The natural resource accounting studies noted above, of the Philippines and Java, required a large input of effort, which it is out of the question to attempt here for the whole of South Asia. Nevertheless, a major objective of this study would be missing if some attempt were not made to estimate the economic cost of land degradation.

It should be stated at the outset that such estimates are highly approximate. They are made with the intention of indicating the orders of magnitude of the costs involved, with the objective of stimulating more detailed studies on a national and local scale.

The best researched cases are the impact of salinization and waterlogging in India and Pakistan (for example Ahmad and Kutcher, 1992; ESCAP, 1990b). A small number of local case studies have been identified, covering impacts of salinization, lowering of the water table, erosion, and soil fertility decline (Vittal *et al.*, 1990; Joshi and Tyagi, 1991; Joshi and Jha, 1992; Chaudhary and Aneja, 1991). It is likely that other such studies exist.

For comparative purposes, the main approaches used here will be those of lost production, nutrient replacement, and reclamation or restoration. The starting point is the estimates for the extent and degree of each type of land degradation obtained in Chapters 4 and 5. Some extremely broad assumptions as to typical yields, yield reductions and farm production economics are necessary. To reduce the problems of differences between prices, types of land use, etc. between countries, in some cases calculations are done first for India (as having more than half the population and agricultural production of the region) and then extended, still more approximately, to the region.

Best estimates for extent of land degradation are given in Table 18. Data on land use, fertilizer use, agricultural production and prices are taken from FAO statistics.

## Assumptions

The term *production loss* refers to the production lost as a result of land degradation, that is:

> Production loss =   production from non-degraded land
> -              production from degraded land, with the same inputs and management

Relative production loss is production loss as a percentage of production from non-degraded land. It should be noted that in many cases, farmers do not accept reduced production but instead, counteract decreased soil productivity by increasing inputs.

The following assumptions are made with respect to the effect of degrees of degradation on agricultural production:

| Degree of degradation | Relative production loss |
|---|---|
| Light | 5% |
| Moderate | 20% |
| Strong | 75% |

These are relatively low, or modest, assumptions; that is to say, the true figures may well be higher. In particular, by definition, strong degradation should mean that the land has been abandoned, with 100% loss of production; however, it has been assumed that 25% has been saved in some way by the ingenuity, backed by need, of the local population.

*The above assumptions are critical*: that is, results for the economic effects of degradation show a high degree of sensitivity, in many cases *pro rata*, to the values assumed.

Generalized prices in the region (1992), taken as the basis for calculations, were taken as:

| | |
|---|---|
| Cereals | US$ 150 per tonne |
| Fertilizer | US$ 300 per tonne nutrients |

## LAND DEGRADATION IN SOUTH ASIA: THE ORDERS OF MAGNITUDE OF THE ECONOMIC COSTS

### Water erosion

**Production loss basis** An estimate will first be made for *India*. Approximately 61% of India's agricultural land is under cereals, with an average yield of 1.9 t/ha. It is assumed that erosion affects cereal-growing land in the same way as total land. On this basis, and with the above assumptions on proportional losses of production, the loss in cereal production is as follows:

| | |
|---|---|
| Light degradation | 168 000 t |
| Moderate degradation | 3 980 000 t |
| Strong degradation | 10 935 000 t |
| | |
| Total cereal production loss | 15 083 000 t |

A production loss of 15 Mt cereals is equivalent to 8% of India's total cereal production.

Assuming similar proportional losses to other forms of production, the 8% loss may be scaled up to 25 Mt cereal equivalent, representative of the loss to total agricultural production.

At an approximate price of US$150 per tonne for cereals or cereal equivalent, the value of lost production is US$2 260 M per year.

For the *region* as a whole, it would be possible to carry out country by country calculations for land use, production, prices, etc., such as were done in the study of Java by Magrath and Arens (1989). Such detail, however, would not be justified in view of the uncertainty of, and sensitivity to, the production losses. An approximation in terms of reduced production as cereal equivalent is:

| | |
|---|---|
| Light degradation | 3 107 000 t |
| Moderate degradation | 13 528 000 t |
| Strong degradation | 19 237 000 t |
| | |
| Total production loss | 35 872 000 t |

A cereal equivalent production loss of 36 Mt is about 9% of the total agricultural production of the region. At a price of US$150 per tonne cereal equivalent, **the value of lost production due to water erosion is US$5 400 M per year**.

This approximate result may be expressed in another way. If all land in the region were non-degraded, that is, in the condition it was in prior to recent population pressure, then with today's level of inputs and methods of management, an additional production of 36 Mt cereal equivalent could be expected in the region.

**Nutrient replacement basis** For the calculation of nutrient replacement it is necessary to estimate current annual rates of erosion associated with degrees of land degradation (the GLASOD survey includes estimates of the extent to which rates of degradation have recently accelerated). The following rates are assumed:

| Degree of degradation | Current rate of erosion |
|---|---|
| Light | 10t/ha per year |
| Moderate | 20t/ha per year |
| Strong | 50t/ha per year |

It is assumed that eroded soil contains 0.2% nutrients. On this basis, for *India*, the annual loss of nutrients through water erosion is:

| | |
|---|---|
| Light degradation | 58 000 t nutrients per year |
| Moderate degradation | 688 000 t nutrients per year |
| Strong degradation | 1 260 000 t nutrients per year |
| Total nutrient loss | 2 006 000 t nutrients per year |

Total mineral fertilizer use in India is 12.5 Mt of nutrients per year. The loss through erosion of 2 Mt is 16% of this. Expressed in another way, India would have to increase its fertilizer use by this amount each year just to replace nutrients lost through erosion.

At a representative fertilizer cost of US$300 per tonne nutrients, the loss through erosion is US$600 M per year.

A similar approximate calculation for the *region* as a whole gives a loss through water erosion of 3.4 Mt nutrients per year. This is equivalent 20% of total fertilizer use in the region. Its value is approximately US$1 020 M per year.

The two estimates obtained for the effect of water erosion are not directly comparable. That obtained for production reflects the cumulative effect of past erosion, whereas the lower estimate based on nutrient replacement is an annual value. However, in replacing the lost nutrients, the farmer is counteracting only of the effects of erosion. These also include loss of soil organic matter and reduction in soil profile depth, leading to degradation of soil physical properties and, in particular, water holding capacity. Nutrient loss, and thus nutrient replacement, is only one element in the effects of erosion.

**Restoration or reclamation** The reclamation of land subject to gully (ravine) erosion is often undertaken, but with the aim of preventing further extension of gullying. Such attempts meet with variable success, and it is rarely possible to restore productivity to anything like its former state.

For land with moderate degradation, a specimen calculation for restoring lost soil is as follows. As above, moderate degradation is assumed to correspond to a current rate of erosion (in excess of replaceable) of 20t/ha per year (equivalent to an horizon thickness of 1.33 mm).

Let it be assumed that replacement of soil by natural processes is at a rate ranging from 0.1-1.0 mm per year, equivalent to 1.5-15.0 t/ha.

To replace the soil lost in one year of erosion at 20t/ha would require fallowing for between 1 and 13 years, and hence a loss of production between 50% and 93%. This is clearly unrealistic as a practical proposition. It indicates, however, that the full cost of erosion is substantially higher than the estimates obtained above, which are on a medium-term basis only. In practical terms, loss of soil material is largely irreversible. To achieve long-term sustainability, erosion must be limited to the rate of soil formation.

**Off-site costs of erosion** Deforestation and erosion lead to greatly increased sediment load in rivers, causing problems of poorer water quality, river bed sedimentation and reservoir sedimentation. A review of the effects of soil conservation measures upon sediment yield is given by Doolette and Magrath (1990, p.203ff.). Reductions in sediment yield through conservation measures are frequently as high as 95%. The economic effect is most clearly seen in sedimentation of reservoirs. For eight Indian reservoirs, the presently assessed life as a percentage of that anticipated on design ranges from 23-79%, with four below 40% (FAO/RAPA, 1992, p.216). In developed countries, off-site costs of erosion are often assessed as substantially higher than on-site costs, although in less developed countries, the reverse may be the case (P. Faeth, D. Knowler, personal communications).

Off-site costs have not been assessed in this study but their existence, and certainly appreciable magnitude, should be taken into account.

## Wind erosion

It is difficult to obtain even the most approximate estimate of the economic cost of wind erosion. The land affected is partly under arable use and partly used for livestock production, and there is virtually no basis for estimating the effects of erosion upon production. Yet if its seriousness is to be appreciated, some value must be given.

If the degree and extent of wind erosion is compared with that of water erosion, the total impact of the two is comparable. Areas affected by moderate and strong wind erosion are similar to those of water erosion, around 35 and 12 M ha respectively. The area for light wind erosion is only 40% of that for water erosion, but on the assumptions used above, this has a relatively small effect on production.

Being confined to dry climates, the average productivity of land affected by wind erosion will be less than that affected by water erosion. Suppose that on average it is one third as productive. The production loss from water erosion was assessed at US$5 400 M per year. For an impact of similar severity, **the production loss from wind erosion is of the order of US$1 800 M per year**.

This impact is very unevenly distributed in the region, being entirely for the countries of the dry zone: Afghanistan, Iran, Pakistan and the dry region of India.

## Soil fertility decline

**Production loss basis** There is no doubt that soil fertility decline is occurring over large parts of the region. Data for assessing its effects are, however, tentative in two respects: the area covered, and the magnitude of the depression of crop yields.

The estimates of area are (as a conservative assumption) dominated by the light degree of degradation, at 38.5 M ha compared with 3.9 M ha affected to moderate or strong degrees. As a further simplifying assumption, the total figure only will be taken, that of 42.4 M ha affected, to at least a light degree, by soil fertility decline.

Two alternative assumptions are then made, which can be justified by the available experimental data. These are that the average effect of fertility to decline is to reduce crop yields, in the absence of additional inputs, by 5% or 10%. Using the same basis as for water erosion, an average cereal equivalent yield of 1.9 t per hectare, gives a production loss of:

For a 5% yield loss:                          4 028 000 t
For a 10% yield loss:                         8 056 000 t

At a price of US$150 per tonne, **the loss to the region from soil fertility decline is tentatively estimated at US$600 M - 1 200 M per year**.

**Replacement cost basis**  As already noted, farmers with soils of declining fertility frequently attempt to maintain yields by additional inputs, primarily fertilizers. Some research results have shown that quite high rates of fertilizer application are necessary where the soil has been degraded by prolonged cropping. However, let it be assumed that on average, yields on the 42.4 Mha of degraded soils can be maintained by an average input of either 50 or 100 kg nutrients per hectare. The cost is taken as US$300 per tonne of nutrients. Additional inputs and their cost are then:

|                        | Fertilizers | Cost |
|------------------------|-------------|------|
| At 50 kg ha[1]:        | 2.12 Mt     | US$636 M |
| At 100 kg ha[1]:       | 4.24 Mt     | US$1 272 M |

This is of the same order of magnitude, US$0.6 - 1.3 billion, as the estimate on a production loss basis.

This reasoning, however, applies only to the short term. The additional of unbalanced fertilizers, without other measures to improve the soil, is a *cause* of fertility decline. Fertilizer rates needed to maintain crop yields can therefore be expected to increase with time, raising the cost.

More fundamental measures are needed to restore soil fertility, particularly through the improvement of organic matter status. These management measures also have a cost, for example the opportunity cost as lost fodder or fuel of returning crop residues to the soil. The combination of such methods for soil improvement with continued, and more balanced, use of fertilizers is necessary for sustained land use in the medium and long term.

**Waterlogging**

Percentage yields obtained under four crops at different water table depths are given in Ahmad and Kutcher (1992, p.42). Taking their own data for areas with shallow water tables, and yield reductions for wheat as representative, this gives a yield loss for *Pakistan* of 1.57 Mt, or about US$240 M per year. On the basis of comparative areas affected, the loss for *India* would be substantially higher. This gives a **total loss from waterlogging in excess of US$500 m per year**.

## Salinization

There have been more attempts to asses the impact of salinization than is the case for other forms of degradation. This is partly because its effects are substantial and visibly apparent, partly because the degree of degradation can be readily quantified, and also because it occurs on irrigated areas which have received large financial investments.

Estimates will first be compared for *Pakistan*. Experimental work on percentage yield losses for different values of salinity is summarized in Ahmad and Kutcher (1992, p.45). The impact differs between crops, with cotton tolerant, rice intolerant of salinity. Taking the data for wheat, and matching values of soil conductivity to degrees of degradation, the following production losses will be assumed:

| Degree of degradation | Relative production loss |
|---|---|
| Light | 15% |
| Moderate | 65% |
| Strong | 100% |

Estimating in terms of wheat equivalent, using the average Pakistan wheat yield of 1.84t/ha, production losses are as follows:

| | |
|---|---|
| Light degradation | 524 000 t |
| Moderate degradation | 1 196 000 t |
| Strong degradation | 2 392 000 t |
| | |
| Total wheat equivalent loss | 4 112 000 t |

Valued at US$150/t wheat this equals a loss of US$617 M per year. These values would be altered by taking the crop mix into account, but the order of magnitude would remain the same.

This may be compared with other estimates. ESCAP (1990b) state, "A 20 per cent reduction in yield of, say, wheat in Pakistan on about 3 M hectares of salt-affected land would result in a loss of about 1.2 M tonnes of grain on a very conservative estimate. This would amount to some US$150 M." Ahmad and Kutcher (1992) assess salinity levels, areas affected and yield decreases for Pakistan, concluding, "If these numbers are anywhere near correct, soil salinity is "robbing" Pakistan of about 25% of its potential production of cotton and rice, or about US$2.5 billion per year!".

It is not possible to obtain comparable estimates for the *region* as a whole. The problem is of the same order of magnitude in *India*, therefore the above estimates may first be doubled, to US$1234 M per year. In areal extent, salinization is dominated by Iran, and the salinized area exceeds that of total arable land. It is therefore difficult to make broad assumptions on which to base an estimate. Taking as a very minimal value a loss of some US$300 M, **the total loss to the region from salinization is not less than US$1 500 M per year.**

**Cost of reclamation**   Salinization and waterlogging can be reversed, and the land productivity partly restored, by reclamation. This has been done most notably in the case of the series of Salinity Control and Reclamation Projects (SCARPs) in Pakistan continuing from 1959 to the present. The main elements in the technology involved are:

- installation of deep drains, to lower the water table;
- leaching of salinized areas, requiring the application of non-saline water in amounts considerably in excess of the irrigation requirement;
- treatment of sodic soils with gypsum.

From 1969-85, SCARP projects covered 3.5 M ha, and a further 2.8 M ha are at present being reclaimed. It is stated that as a result of SCARPs, soil salinity has been reduced from 40% to 28%, and 80 000 ha of land are being restored to production each year (ESCAP, 1989b; 1990b, p. 26).

The cost of such reclamation measures is huge. The opportunity cost of the water used for leaching is that of the production it could have given if used for irrigation. Reclamation costs are currently about US$500/ha (Ahmad and Kutcher, 1992). For *Pakistan*, the cost of reclaiming 3.3 M hectares of affected land has been estimated at US$9 billion (Ahmad and Kutcher, 1992). With an area affected of the same magnitude, the cost to *India* would be similar.

The cost of reclaiming salinized and waterlogged areas is considerably higher than that of prevention by good design and management of irrigation schemes.

## Lowering of the water table

The consequence of lowering of the water table, where it has developed in areas of non-saline groundwater, could be expressed in economic terms as the added cost of tubewell pumping from greater depth. The true shadow price of electricity, and not its subsidized price, should be used. It is likely that large farmers can afford this added cost, and that the more serious effect is upon small farmers with holdings, and capital resources, too small to justify deep tubewells.

A production loss basis would underestimate the cost of lowering the water table, since this is a clear case of non-sustainable use of a resource. *Restoration* of water table levels would require reduction in water use to less than the rate of natural recharge, with consequent loss of production, for long periods. This is an unrealistic scenario, and the economic cost would be vast. Because of these complexities, coupled with inadequate data, the cost of lowering the water table has not been assessed in this study.

## MACROECONOMIC IMPACT OF LAND DEGRADATION

### Summary

The difficulties and uncertainties that arise in assessing the economic effects of land degradation must again be emphasized. Sources of error arise at all stages of assessment:

1.      Estimates of the extent and severity of degradation.

2.     Assessment of the physical effects, primarily upon land productivity, of a given severity of degradation.
3.     Conversion of the physical effects into economic terms.

These sources of error are cumulative: an over- or under-assessment at one stage is multiplied by errors at successive stages. For stages 1 and 2, the sensitivity of the total estimate is almost *pro rata* with errors of estimate. If the area affected by a given extent and severity of degradation is over- or underestimated by 50%, the deduced economic impact will be underestimated by the same amount. For the physical effects the relation is somewhat less simple, for example, total loss of land reduces inputs as well as production, but the sensitivity of the final economic result to the proportional loss of production is still high.

It would be possible to argue that the overall degree or uncertainty is such that no total figure should be quoted. To do this would be to miss the objective of this analysis, which is to signal that the problem of land degradation appears, on present evidence, to be of a magnitude that is significant in relation to the total wealth of the countries concerned.

Using the incomplete data above, and basing a summary on the method of lost production, the estimates are given in Table 21.

Summing these estimates for the direct, on-site, costs gives a total of US$9.8 - US$11 billion per year. Thus, in round figures, the cumulative effect of human-induced land degradation is estimated to cost countries of the region a sum of the order of US$10 billion per year.

TABLE 21
**Provisional estimates of the cost of land degradation in the region**

| Type of degradation | Cost, billion US$ per year | Notes |
|---|---|---|
| Water erosion | 5.4 | On-site effects only |
| Wind erosion | 1.8 | Assessed relative to water erosion |
| Fertility decline | 0.6-1.2 | Tentative estimate |
| Waterlogging | 0.5 | |
| Salinization | 1.5 | |
| Lowering of water table | | Not assessed |

The gross domestic product of the eight countries (1989) is US$488B, and their combined agricultural domestic product US$145 billion. The estimate obtained for the on-site effects of land degradation upon productivity is equivalent to 2% of the gross domestic product of the region, or 7% of its agricultural gross domestic product. The inclusion of off-site effects of water erosion would increase this value substantially.

**The value of resources**

The above discussion has been conducted largely on the basis of the user value of land resources, their value for agricultural production. There are, in addition, values which are not directly quantifiable but which are known. For example, a soil cover is needed to stabilize runoff and provide base flow; where there is no such cover, runoff is immediate as floods. There are also user values which are not yet known; for example, a century ago, the resource potential of bauxitic soils was not appreciated.

However, natural resources also possess a *primary value* over and above the sum of their user, or secondary, values. In the case of soils, the primary value represents the outcome of processes of soil formation - rock weathering, pedogenesis, biological activity - which have taken of the order of 10 000 - 100 000 years. Within the human time span, soil cannot be created (other than in extremely small amounts). The primary value represents the difference between land without soil and land with soil. For plant resources, the primary value includes the processes of evolution.

The primary value of soils is not only to the present generation, nor to the 20-50 years commonly included in obtaining net *present* values by the procedure of cash flow discounting. Soils have been a resource for the past 2000 and more years. There is no reason to support that the population will not be dependent upon them for a least the same length of time into the future. Moreover, if there is continued population increase, land resources will certainly increase in relative value in the future.

Complex questions of economic analysis are involved in assessing primary values, which it is inappropriate to discuss here. One simple means of obtaining a minimum figure is to estimate the sum of today's user values and multiply this by, say, 2 000 without discounting. This represents **the value to future generations of today's soil resources**. Whilst not attempting such an assessment here, the essential point is that land resources have a value, for future generations, over and above the sum of either their current user values, or their discounted net present value.

## Discussion

The existence of a 'contrary' view has already been noted. Expressed in terms of investment appraisal, this states that reports of land degradation may be greatly exaggerated; and that unless and until better data are obtained, the problem does not meet the criteria for development investment.

For reasons given in Chapter 5, Section *Discussion,* this view is rejected. The present study does not seek to magnify the seriousness of the problem. It is an attempt to obtain the best objective estimates on the basis of available data. The assumptions made in calculation of economic values err on the side of caution. On this basis, **the best estimate that can be obtained is that land degradation is costing countries of the region an economic loss of the order no less than US$10 billion, equivalent to 7% of their combined agricultural gross domestic product**.

Efforts should certainly be made to improve the quality of the data, not only on the degree of degradation but also its effects upon production. However, action to check degradation should not be withheld until such improved data are available. The loss of productive resources is already considerable and is becoming more serious year by year.

# Chapter 8

# Effects upon the people

In Chapter 6, an attempt was made at a costing of the effects of land degradation considered on a macroeconomic basis, at the national and regional levels. This chapter considers the effects upon the people. These can be called social effects but, since an adequate income is a primary concern of farmers, they are also economic effects, at the microeconomic or farm economics level.

The effect will be considered at two stages: effects upon production, and consequences for the people.

## EFFECTS UPON PRODUCTION

Land degradation affects crop production, livestock production, and forest production. The consequences differ according to the type and degree of degradation.

**Total abandonment of land**  Where degradation reaches the severe degree, formerly productive land must be abandoned. Examples where this is clearly seen are:

□  Salinization patches, e.g. in India and Pakistan, where the outlines of fields can still be seen in areas where whole farms have been abandoned. Large tracts of land have totally gone out of production.

□  Gullies, e.g. in the Pothwar Plateau of Pakistan, where former cropland is literally carried away, leaving a wilderness of ravines.

□  Total removal of the soil from steep slopes, e.g. in parts of the hill country of Sri Lanka, where former tea cultivation has been abandoned and the land colonized by grassland of low productive potential.

The initial abandonment of land takes place when, although some growth of crops is still possible, yields are so low.

**Reduced crop yields**  Where land has been subject to light or moderate degradation, the same level of inputs will give lower outputs. These may be reduced crop yields or lower livestock production.

Relatively little precise data is yet available on lowering of production as a result of water and wind erosion. The question is being studied in a FAO research network, although this does not at present include countries of the region (FAO, 1991b). For Andhra Pradesh, India, a study based on artificial removal of topsoil showed clear and strong relations between topsoil depth and crop yields, the slope of the loss curve being greater for high-rainfall than low-rainfall years (Vittal *et al.*, 1990). Data for yield losses consequent upon soil fertility decline have been given in Chapter 3. Reductions in crop yield due to salinity has been well researched, with percentage losses differing as between salt sensitive and tolerant crops (e.g. Ahmad and Kutchler, 1992; Joshi and Jha, 1992).

For rangelands, a reduction in livestock productivity to 10-50 percent of its potential is estimated for desertified rangelands of Pakistan (Asian Development Bank, 1992a). Other countries of the dry zone report similar effects.

Forest productivity is also reduced on degraded land, although this is mitigated by the capacity of some tree species to tolerate poor soils, and the recuperative effects upon soil of appropriate reforestation.

**Increased inputs and greater costs**  The level of poverty of many farmers is such that they cannot accept the consequence of reduced yields. Instead, they must attempt to maintain their food supplies from the degraded land, by means of increased inputs. This is now widely the case where attempts are made to combat soil fertility decline by increased inputs of fertilizers. Another response is to attempt to maintain livestock numbers despite a reduced carrying capacity of pastures, thus leading to a vicious circle of further degradation.

**Reduced responses to inputs**  It is now accepted that fertilizers are best utilized by application of low to moderate amounts, whilst seeking to obtain high responses. Land degradation, particularly the lowering of soil organic matter, has the opposite effect, that of lowering fertilizer responses.

**Reduced productivity on irrigated land**  A specific case of lower crop yields and reduced responses to inputs occurs on the irrigated lands which are widespread in the region. These irrigation systems have been established at high cost, whether of capital, as in tubewells and the large reservoir and canal schemes, or labour, as in the cases of hand-dug wells and earth dams. Lowered productivity, as a result of soil fertility decline, waterlogging and salinization, reduces the benefits from irrigation, leading to less efficient use of capital and labour inputs.

**Loss of flexibility in land management**  Reduced crop yields can force farmers to grow only basic food crops, particularly cereals (Joshi and Jha, 1992). Again there is a feedback effect, since continuous cereal production causes further decline in soil fertility.

**Greater risk**  Degraded land is less resilient, less able to recover from recurrent disasters, such as drought. One of the major effects of erosion is reduced water-holding capacity of the soil. Increase in risk places constraints on land management, making farmers reluctant to use up scarce capital on fertilizers.

**Loss of water for irrigation**  An off-site effect of deforestation and erosion of watershed areas is destabilization of river flow regimes, causing flooding after rains and reduced flows in subsequent dry periods. Where there are downstream irrigation systems, this reduces water availability at times when it is most needed.

Lowering of the water table increases irrigation costs, and can make groundwater totally unavailable to farmers with small landholding, who cannot afford deep tubewells.

**Diversion of resources to reclamation**   As already noted with respect to fertilizer inputs, pressure of need forces farmers to make great efforts in an attempt to maintain production. Thus they may construct gabions across gullies, or build terraces with lines of stones, requiring large amounts of labour, or construct deeper tubewells. This has been called 'defensive expenditure'. All such inputs, whether of labour or capital, carry an opportunity cost, that of the alternative, productive, uses to which the resources could have been applied.

## CONSEQUENCES FOR THE PEOPLE

The effects of land degradation upon production have impacts upon agricultural population, whether engaged in crop production, livestock production, or dependent upon forest products.

**Increased landlessness**   Landlessness among the rural population is a problem of vast scale in parts of the region (Sinha, 1984). The causes are many, among which abandonment of degraded land is only one. It is probably a minor cause in statistical terms - but does not seem so to the farmers who have lost their land!

**Lower and less reliable food supplies**   Lowering of crop yields means reduced production of food crops; increased risk means lowered food security.

**Increased labour requirements**   Reduced crop yields and increased inputs both have the effect of reducing the farmers' returns from labour. Labour used in reclamation and rehabilitation of land is labour lost from production.

A direct consequence is the effect of deforestation on labour needed to collect fuelwood. In parts of the Himalayan mountain belt, deforestation has forced farmers (often women) to walk great distances to collect fuelwood. The drying up of rivers caused by destabilized flow, and the lowering of groundwater, similarly increase labour needed for water collection.

**Lower incomes**   Out of all the consequences of land degradation, the most serious for the rural population of the region is lower incomes. These result from either or both of the factors noted above: increased inputs or reduced outputs.

In classical economic theory, 'land' was considered as a fixed resource, to which the factors of labour and capital were applied. With land degradation occurring it becomes a declining resource, and as a consequence, labour and capital are less efficiently applied and productivity is lowered.

If most farmers do not know about economic theory, they are very well aware of it in practice! Land degradation means that they must either accept a lowered productivity, of food and other requirements, or else put in greater effort and resources to maintain production.

## LAND DEGRADATION AND THE POOR

Whenever adverse changes occur in the less developed world, it is usually the poor who suffer most. This situation arises from the very definition of the poor, those who lack adequate access to the basic necessities of life and the resources needed to obtain them.

This is certainly the case with land degradation. In the past rural population, however low their incomes may seem in modern terms, had access to adequate land to meet their needs. When a disaster, such as flood, drought, attack by pests, or war, destroyed their normal means of livelihood, there were spare land resources to fall back upon. They could take new land into cultivation, kill the few livestock they possessed which fed upon natural pastures, or go into the forest and extract roots or hunt wildlife.

Because of land shortage, accentuated by degradation, these options are no longer available. Farmers with less than one hectare are dependent on that small area for all of their agricultural income. They are surrounded by other farms, such common rangeland or woodland as there may be is degraded and of low productivity, and over large areas there is no forest left at all. The only alternatives open are to work on the land for others, non-agricultural occupations, migration to the cities, or ultimately, dependence on famine relief.

It is in these tightly constrained circumstances that land degradation hurts most. Production begins to fall. Because production is close to the limit for supplying basic needs, a response must be made to secure these needs in the short term. This may be clearance of fragile lands, for the sustainable management of which, poor farmers lack the resources. It may be increased inputs, particularly the attempt to maintain yields by nitrogen fertilizers. The non-sustainable land management leads to further degradation.

Larger farmers are less likely to degrade land. Certainly, cases are known where irresponsible rich farmers exploit the land, but by and large they will conserve their resources. When disasters occur, they can tighten their belts, turn to alternative sources of income, or borrow and repay in better years. These options are not open to the poor.

It is they who, through force of circumstances, play the greatest part in the causal nexus of land, population, poverty, and degradation (Figure 9, p. 57). It is the poor who suffer most from land degradation.

# Chapter 9

# Institutions and programmes
# to combat degradation

Whilst problems of the environment do not recognize international frontiers, efforts to combat land degradation must be based largely upon national institutions. This applies not only to work undertaken at the national level, for example soil conservation programmes, but to regional and international efforts, which must be largely applied through national institutions.

A short review can consist only of brief indications of the major institutions, their mandate and work. In many cases where the functions are implicit, the name only is given. Institutions are divided broadly into research and implementation. Research institutions are those of which the primary function is the acquisition of knowledge, implementation institutions those charged with putting into practice measures to combat degradation.

Most national institutions are known in their respective countries by acronyms, but these are given here only for international organizations.

The constraint of time has meant that these summaries have not been reviewed by governments of the countries concerned. Whilst every effort has been made, they doubtless contain omissions. They should therefore be treated as indicative, not comprehensive.


## NATIONAL INSTITUTIONS

### Afghanistan

For 14 years, Afghanistan has been torn by war and political instability. Besides destruction of resources, this has made the task of institutions extremely difficult. Whilst some efforts are being made in the present difficult circumstances, most land rehabilitation must await restoration of stable political conditions.

The present limited institutional structure includes:

Ministry of Planning
Ministry of Agriculture and Land Reform

International institutions which provide constrained but active support include ADB, ESCAP, FAO, IMF and the World Bank. A report was made to the UNCED conference (Afghanistan, Ministry of Planning, 1992).

## Bangladesh

Five ministries are concerned, directly or indirectly, with affairs of land, the Ministries of Agriculture, Environment and Forests, Rural Development and Cooperatives, Planning, and Food.

The *Bangladesh Agricultural Research Council* coordinates work of the *Bangladesh Agricultural Institute*, four crop-based institutes (for rice, jute, sugar cane and tea) and an institute for nuclear research.

The *Soil Resource Development Institute* is a separate institute concerned with inventory and evaluation of soil resources; it also transfers knowledge for extension purposes. With international cooperation, the Institute has acquired a considerable amount of detailed information, and is the main repository of knowledge on land resources of the country.

The *Bangladesh Water Development Board* manages flood protection, drainage and irrigation projects, and is concerned with land and water use. The *Land Reclamation Directorate* functions under this Board. The *Bangladesh Institute of Development Studies* conducts research in economics, demography and social sciences, including in relation to agriculture and land. The *Hill Tract Development Board* is concerned with most aspects of development specific to the hill areas. Other relevant research institutes include the *Bangladesh Forest Research Institute*, the *Bangladesh Livestock Research Institute*, and agricultural universities.

Extension and implementation are conducted by the *Department of Agricultural Extension*, the *Forest Department*, the *Department of Environment*, the *Bangladesh Rural Development Board*, the *Bangladesh Water Development Board*, the *Land and Water Use Directorate*, and the *Department of Irrigation Water Development and Flood Control*.

The *Department of Environment* was strengthened in 1985, and is responsible for environmental impact assessments.

During this short review, the impression was gained that there is some overlap of responsibilities within the area of land resources.

## Bhutan

Because of its small population, the institutional structure of Bhutan is simple. The *National Planning Agency* formulates policy guidelines. The *Department of Agriculture* includes a *Research and Extension Division*, within which there is a *Soil Fertility Unit*.

## India

Because of its population and size, federal structure, and for historical reasons, there are a large number of institutions active in the area of land resources in India, and the following account is selective.

At national level the relevant ministries are the *Ministries of Agriculture, Rural Development*, and *Environment and Forests, and Water Resources*, together with the *Planning Commission*, a body of cabinet level.

The *Indian Council of Agricultural Research* is the apex body for research and education in all aspects of the agricultural sciences. It has 43 institutes, 4 national bureaux, 21 national research centres, 9 project directorates, and currently operates over 70 All India Coordinated Research Projects. The *Indian Council of Forestry Research and Education* performs corresponding functions in the field of forestry.

Research institutes of particular relevance to land resources, conservation and degradation include, at the national level:

*Indian Agricultural Research Institute*
*National Bureau of Soil Survey and Land Use Planning*
*Central Soil and Water Conservation Research and Training Institute*
*Central Soil Salinity Research Institute*
*Central Research Institute for Dryland Agriculture*
*Central Arid Zone Research Institute*
*ICAR Research Complex for the North-Eastern Hills Region*
*Indian Institute of Soil Science*
*Indian Grassland and Fodder Research Institute*
*Directorate of Water Management*
*National Research Centre for Agroforestry*

The *National Bureau of Soil Survey and Land Use Planning* is the primary institute for basic knowledge of land resources and their management at the national level. Applied knowledge is found within the respective institutes listed above, for example, soil salinization within the *Central Soil Salinity Research Institute*.

At the state level, some states have Water and Land Management Institutes, Forest Research Institutes, Irrigation Research Institutes, and Agricultural Universities.

Some of the All India Coordinated Research Projects having particular relevance to land degradation are:

Management of salt affected soils and use of saline water in agriculture
Micro and secondary nutrients and pollutants in soils and plants
Microbial decomposition and recycling of organic wastes
Soil physical conditions to increase agricultural production in problem areas
Soil test crop response correlation
Agroforestry
Forage crops
Agricultural drainage

In development, the *National Wastelands Development Board* has the aim of bringing wastelands (in large part, degraded lands) into productive use, through afforestation and other measures. A *National Land Use and Conservation Board* formulates policy papers for the apex body, the *National Land Use and Wasteland Development Council*.

The *Soil and Water Conservation Division* in the Ministry of Agriculture plays a key role in the implementation of integrated watershed management programmes. These are planned to cover 86 M ha, of which 26 M ha of highly critical areas have been taken up on a priority basis. These priority watersheds were identified by the *All India Soil and Land Use Survey*.[1]

The first line in agricultural extension is implementation through 109 *Krishi Vigyan Kendras* ('Agricultural Knowledge Centres'), supported by *National Demonstration Projects* and *Operational Research Projects*. The *Central Water Commission*, under the Ministry of Water Resources, is concerned with the development and utilization of water resources. Implementation is further carried out through *State Departments of Agriculture, Soil Conservation, Forestry*, and *Animal Husbandry*.

Among numerous non-governmental organizations, of particular relevance to land degradation is the *Society for Promotion of Wastelands Development*.

Whilst this may appear to be a complex institutional structure, it must be remembered that it serves over one fifth of the world's agricultural population. In many cases, responsibilities are relatively well defined, although cases of overlap will be apparent.

## Iran[2]

The principal institution concerned with land degradation is the *Bureau of Sand Dune Fixation and Combating Desertification*, a unit of the *Forestry and Range Organization* within the *Ministry of Jihad-e-Sazandegi*. Other relevant bodies include the *Department of the Environment*, the *Research Institute of Forest and Rangeland*, and a *Working Group on Agricultural Meteorology* within the *Meteorological Organization*.

## Nepal

At the level of strategic planning, an *Environment Protection Council* has been established to coordinate efforts. Relevant ministries are the *Ministry of Forest and Soil Conservation*, the *Ministry of Agriculture*, and the *Ministry of Water Supply*.

Research is coordinated by the *Nepal Agricultural Research Council*. Relevant bodies and activities include the *Central Soil Science Division*, the *Integrated Soil Survey Project*, the *National Pasture and Fodder Research Division*, and the *Soil and Plant Nutrition Improvement Project*.

In development, the nodal institution is the *Department of Soil Conservation and Watershed Management*, under the Ministry of Forests and Soil Conservation. Other relevant bodies include the *Department of Agriculture, Department of Irrigation, Department of Forests*, and the *Soil Fertility Advisory Unit*.

---

[1]     This function distinguishes it from the previously mentioned body of apparently similar name, the National Bureau of Soil Survey and Land Use Planning.

[2]     Owing to constraints, it has not been possible to obtain a full account of institutional structure for Iran.

## Pakistan

Strategic planning is undertaken by the *National Conservation Strategy Unit* of the *Environment and Urban Affairs Division* (an independent Ministry, currently with one division). This unit works in collaboration with the *World Conservation Union.*

Research is coordinated by the *Pakistan Agriculture Research Council.* Key institutes involved in land degradation and conservation research include:

*Land Resources Section* of the *National Agricultural Research Centre*
*Soil Survey of Pakistan*
*Soil and Water Conservation Research Institution, Punjab*
*National Fertilizer Development Centre*
*Arid Zone Research Institute*
*International Waterlogging and Salinity Research Institute*, part of the *Water and Power Development Authority*
*Soil Salinity Research Institute, Punjab*
*Drainage and Reclamation Institute of Pakistan*
*Pakistan Forest Institute*
*Irrigation Research Institute*
*Range Research Stations* (provincial)

Within the irrigated lands, planning and development are controlled by the *Water and Power Development Authority*. Of major importance are the *Salinity Control and Reclamation Projects*. Other implementation is carried out at provincial level, by provincial *Directorates* and *Departments* of *Soil Conservation, Forestry*, and *Irrigation*. Forestry is coordinated at the national level by the *Inspector General of Forests*.

## Sri Lanka

Ministerial responsibility is divided between the *Ministry of Environment and Parliamentary Affairs*, which has a coordinating role; the *Ministry of Lands, Irrigation and Mahaweli Development*; and the *Ministry of Agricultural Development and Research*. The Government obtains information and cooperation on environmental planning from the *Geography Department, University of Peredeniya*.

The key research institution is the *Land and Water Management Centre* of the *Central Agricultural Research Institute*. Other research is conducted by commodity institutes, for example the *Tea Research Institute* is active in soil conservation and agroforestry research.

Development institutes include the *Land Use Policy and Planning Division* and the *Upper Mahaweli Environment and Forest Conservation Division* of the *Mahaweli Authority*. Environmental impact assessments are the responsibility of the *Central Environmental Authority*. Agricultural extension has recently been decentralized.

This is by no means a full list. It is recognized within Sri Lanka that the institutional structure within the area of land resources is complex, and with some overlapping responsibilities. The position has been contrasted with that in coastal conservation where one body, the Coast Conservation Department, has responsibility, legal powers, and is able to take effective action.

## NATIONAL INSTITUTIONS: DISCUSSION

The institutional structures of the various countries have developed differently with time, for a variety of reasons. It is difficult to comment on them as a whole, but some generalizations may be made.

There is a tendency towards unduly complex structures, with overlapping responsibilities. Problems arise in linking activities of the 'line divisions', Departments of Agriculture, Forestry, and Livestock Production, with the various bodies concerned with environment, conservation, and land use planning.

Research and, especially, planning are often more advanced and active than actual implementation in the field. It is so much easier to make a watershed management plan, for example, than to implement it. There would be benefits if those engaged in research in land degradation and conservation were on occasion to take some active part in implementation; and conversely, for feedback from field extension staff to be more fully incorporated into planning.

The area of environmental considerations is now so wide that at the level of central environmental authorities, it would be useful to recognize divisions, or areas of responsibility, within it. *Land resources* is one such major area. Other divisions might cover, for example, environmental pollution, the marine environment, and the urban environment. Land resources covers the sustainable use of the resources of climate, water, soils, landform and vegetation, combining productive use in agriculture, including livestock production, and forestry, with conservation.

Countries should seek to clarify institutional responsibilities in the area of land resources.

## ENVIRONMENTAL LEGISLATION

It is recognized that environmental legislation has an important role to play in combatting land degradation. It has not been possible in this study to cover the state of legislation in different countries. A review is given in ESCAP (1990a, pp.185-200). This includes a summary table, "Status of land use and resource conservation legislation" in which the countries of the present study are classified as follows:

| | |
|---|---|
| Extensive coverage: | None |
| Moderate coverage: | Bangladesh, India, Sri Lanka |
| Minimal coverage: | Nepal, Pakistan |
| Not included in the assessment: | Afghanistan, Bhutan, Iran. |

Two features are widely found in environmental legislation. First, the provisions of environmental laws (e.g. of soil conservation, forestry) often require revision to take account of changing circumstances. Secondly, difficulties are invariably experienced in enforcement of the legal requirements.

## INTERNATIONAL INSTITUTIONS IN THE REGION

Most of the major international institutions are active within the region, notably FAO, ESCAP, UNEP, UNDP, the World Bank, the International Monetary Fund, and the Asian Development Bank.

Many of the research institutions with headquarters in other parts of the world have stations, networks or cooperative programmes there. Note may be taken of those major international institutions which have headquarters in the region and which therefore, although their primary responsibilities are international, make particular contributions regionally, including through country collaborative programmes. These are:

*International Centre for Research in the Semi-Arid Tropics* (Hyderabad, India)
*International Irrigation Management Institute* (Kandy, Sri Lanka)
*International Centre for Integrated Mountain Development* (Kathmandu, Nepal)

The *World Conservation Union* collaborates in the planning of environmental conservation in several countries of the region.

## REGIONAL COLLABORATIVE PROGRAMMES

Two regional collaborative programmes, both ongoing, have made considerable contributions to the coordination of knowledge on land resources, degradation and conservation, and to providing policy guidelines of action.

**Asian Network on Problem Soils**  This is organized by FAO through its Regional Office for Asia and the Pacific (RAPA), located in Bangkok. Formed in 1989, this covers the FAO Asia and Pacific region, which includes six of the eight countries of the South Asian region covered in this report (excluding Afghanistan and Iran).

The network holds meetings every two years. Reports have been produced on the 1989 meeting, *Problem soils of Asia and the Pacific* (FAO/RAPA, 1990), and the 1991 meeting, *Environmental issues in land and water development* (FAO/RAPA, 1992). A third meeting will take place in 1993 on *Collection and analysis of land degradation data*, as recommended by the 21st FAO Regional Conference for Asia and the Pacific.

**Desertification Control in Asia and the Pacific (DESCONAP)**  This is organized by the Economic and Social Council for Asia and the Pacific (ESCAP). It includes all countries of the present South Asia region. Outputs from its meetings include *Problems and prospects of desertification control in the ESCAP region* (ESCAP, 1983) and *Desertification through wind erosion and its control in Asia and the Pacific* (ESCAP, 1991b).

ESCAP issues a newsletter, *ESCAP Environment News*.

**Fertilizer and Development Network for Asia and the Pacific (FADINAP)**  This network is concerned with fertilizer production, trade and use. Of special relevance to land degradation is its 1992 meeting, *Fertilization and the Environment* (Pradhan, 1992; Tandon, 1992).

**Forestry Research Support Programme for Asia and the Pacific (FORSPA)**  This is organized by FAO through its RAPA office. Its work is summarized in *Forestry Research in the Asia-Pacific* (FAO/FORSPA, 1992). Aspects of its work of particular relevance to land degradation are tropical deforestation, forestry's role in sustaining agricultural productivity, management of fragile tropical soils, fuelwood, and forestry and the environment. A newsletter is issued, *Info FORSPA*.

**Asian Bio and Organic Fertilizer Network**  Organized by FAO through RAPA, this led to the production of *Organic recycling in Asia and the Pacific* (FAO/RAPA, 1991).

These networks continue to play an important role in exchange of scientific knowledge and formulation of policy and programmes.

# Chapter 10

# Conclusions and proposals

## CONCLUSIONS FROM THE STUDY

Some major conclusions reached in this study are:

1.  Land degradation has taken place within the context of a high density of population in relation to available land. Very little land capable of sustainable agricultural production remains which is not already under use. The continuing population increase means that this situation is becoming more severe every year.

2.  Different estimates of the extent and severity of degradation differ widely, often by factors of two or more. The basic reasons are:

    □ Failure to define what is meant by the degrees of degradation described, in quantitative terms which can be objectively determined and mapped.
    □ The absence of surveys of the extent of degradation, and lack of monitoring of changes in land resources.

    An exception to these generalizations are the definitions of degrees of salinization, and the surveys and monitoring of its changes carried out in some areas.

3.  Despite these problems with data, the view that evidence for land degradation is insufficient to justify immediate action is rejected. Although quantitative estimates differ, **the weight of evidence is clear that land degradation in the region is widespread, and has reached a severe degree in many areas.** Environmental 'disaster areas' have occurred already, for example areas of severe and extensive salinization in parts of the irrigated Indus and Ganges plains. Others are predicted, most notably the severe deforestation and water erosion in the mountain and hill areas of Nepal.

4.  Best estimates of the areas affected by light, moderate and severe degrees of degradation have been given in Tables 18 and 19. The relative severity of different types of land degradation in the region in the countries of the region is summarized in Table 22.

5.  The countries of the dry zone - Afghanistan, Iran, Pakistan and the western part or India - are severely affected by water and wind erosion, soil fertility decline, deforestation, rangeland degradation and desertification. Their alluvial plain and basin areas are affected by waterlogging, salinization and lowering of the water table.

TABLE 22
**Severity of land degradation in the countries of the region**

| | Afghanistan | Bangladesh | Bhutan | India | | Iran | Nepal | Pakistan | Sri Lanka |
|---|---|---|---|---|---|---|---|---|---|
| | | | | Dry region | Humid region | | | | |
| Water erosion | XX | X | - | XX | XX | XX | XX | XX | XX |
| Wind erosion | X | - | - | XX | - | XX | - | XX | - |
| Soil fertility decline | - | XX | - | - | XX | - | - | XX | XX |
| Waterlogging | - | - | - | XX | - | X | - | X | - |
| Salinization | X | - | - | XX | - | XX | - | XX | - |
| Lowering of the water table | - | - | - | X | - | XX | - | - | - |
| Deforestation | XX | XX | X | X | X | X | XX | XX | X |
| Rangeland degradation | XX | - | - | XX | - | XX | - | XX | - |

X = Moderately severe.
XX = Very severe.

Four countries of the humid zone - Bangladesh, Nepal, Sri Lanka and the greater part of India - are severely affected by water erosion on their rainfed lands, by soil fertility decline, and by deforestation. In parts of the hill and mountain areas of Nepal, deforestation and water erosion have reached an extreme degree. Bhutan, because of its lower population density, has not yet suffered severe land degradation, but deforestation, often the initial cause of degradation, is taking place.

6.     The problem of **soil fertility decline** has not previously received sufficient attention. A fundamental cause is the attempt to maintain crop yields through application of fertilizers, without also taking other fundamental measures of soil management, principally maintenance of soil organic matter status. This form of degradation is found in both the humid and dry zones.

7.     The **direct causes** of land degradation are inappropriate methods of land management. The **underlying causes** stem from the interaction of land resources with economic and social conditions. There is a causal nexus between land shortage, population increase, poverty, and land degradation (Figure 9, p. 62).

8.     In very broad, order of magnitude, terms, the economic cost of land degradation can be estimated, mainly on a production loss basis. For the region as a whole, the cost is put at US$ 10 billion per year, or 7% of agricultural gross domestic product (Table 21, p. 75).

9.     The effects of land degradation upon the people of the region are widespread and, in some cases, severe. Some farmers have totally lost their land. On croplands, a far larger number have experienced lower crop yields or, in the attempt to maintain yields on an impoverished land base, increased costs of inputs. On rangelands, livestock production levels have been very severely reduced.

The combined effect has been to cause lower incomes. The impact of land degradation is greatest on the poor.

10. Land degradation is not simply a problem of environment, but also one of production. It affects the ability of people of the region to obtain food and other basis necessities. Degradation is thus a problem of sustainability, the combination of production with conservation of the natural resources on which maintenance of production in the future depends.

11. Institutional structures to combat land degradation exist in all countries of the region. These offer much potential, both for research and implementation. Some countries possess an unduly complex structure, sometimes with poorly defined or overlapping responsibilities. There is a need to recognize land resources, productivity and degradation as a distinctive field, and clarify responsibilities for research, survey, monitoring and implementation.

## PROPOSALS: INTRODUCTION

The proposals arise from the above conclusions. They are confined to the main lines of approach and action. Many of the proposed actions will initially require discussion on a regional, and in some cases international, basis, in order to secure uniformity of methods. They will subsequently require modifications in detail to meet the circumstances of different countries.

If integrated action is not taken, to combat both the direct and the indirect causes of land degradation:

□ resources will be destroyed, in some cases irreversibly;
□ there will be further considerable economic losses at the national level;
□ the people, mainly the poor, will suffer.

A prerequisite for effective action is recognition, by national governments, of the severity of land degradation and its effects upon the people and the national economies. It is not sufficient to pay lip service to 'environment' nor to write reports. There must be allocation of staff, budget and resources.

The proposals fall into two groups:

□ Assessment of the severity and extent of the problem, and its effects (Proposals 1-4).
□ Action to check and reverse land degradation (Proposals 5-7).

Problems of land degradation have already been considered within the FAO/RAPA Asian Problem Soils Network and the ESCAP Desertification Control Network. Following the two recent conferences of the former, a position paper was produced which includes detailed recommendations for action. Whilst written with respect to the whole of Asia and the Pacific, it is certainly applicable to the present South Asian Region. The recommendations in that paper are given under the heading, "A framework for action" (Dent *et al.*, 1992, pp.20-26). They are fully in agreement with the proposals of the present study. They amplify and expand these with respect to development of national institutions and improved methods of land use management (training and implementation), and contain additional material on people's participation.

## PROPOSALS FOR STRENGTHENING EFFORTS TO COMBAT LAND DEGRADATION

### Proposal 1   Practical definitions of degrees of severity of land degradation

In order to acquire more accurate data, it is first necessary to define the degrees of land degradation, in terms that offer practical means of observation, monitoring and mapping. An early attempt to do so was made by FAO (1979). The definitions employed in the GLASOD survey (Table 4, p. 24) provide a valid starting point, but these need to be converted to quantitative form.

This action is best taken at *international* level.

### Proposal 2   Establishment of a regional programme and guidelines for survey of land degradation, and monitoring of change

If surveys are to be conducted nationally, it is first necessary to establish detailed objectives, methods and priorities are a *regional* level. The programme should include:

□   **Survey** of the present state of degradation.
□   **Monitoring** of soil changes. A discussion, with outline of methods and examples, is given in Young (1991).

An FAO/RAPA meeting is scheduled for 1993 which will give initial consideration to such a programme.

### Proposal 3   Study of the economic and social effects upon the people

Very few specific studies of this nature were identified in the course of the present review. Ideally, such work should be conducted in parallel with physical surveys, and include cooperation in the field between soil scientists and social scientists.

The methodology for study of economic consequences at the macroeconomic level, and of economic and social effects upon the people, is less well established than that for physical surveys. Initial consideration at *international* level would be preferable.

### Proposal 4   Translation of these guidelines (Proposals 3 and 4) into national programmes.

This is clearly a matter for action at *national* level. Among aspects to be covered are:

□   **Clarify institutional responsibilities**  It may be necessary to establish a high-level advisory committee on land degradation policy. This body should then seek, through collaboration with the Ministries and Departments concerned, to clarify responsibilities in areas of research, planning and implementation.

It is desirable that countries should identify one **nodal institution** for land degradation affairs as a whole, together with others with defined responsibilities for particular types of degradation and aspects of research, planning and implementation.

□    **Identify priorities**  In all countries there are critical aspects, where land degradation and its consequences have already reached serious proportions or threaten to do so. In some cases these will be specific land regional areas, such as those with particularly severe erosion or salinization. In others, a priority may arise in the existence of a problem of moderate degree but occurring over a large area, such as soil fertility decline.

□ ·  **Plan and carry out national programmes**  It is at this point that the international, regional and national activities set out above will be put into practice.

**Priority 5    Research into measures to combat degradation.**

Practical field implementation needs to be continuously supported by research. Aspects which require particular attention include:

□    practical methods of improving and maintaining soil organic matter status;
□    ways of securing participation of the people in the implementation of improved measures of land management, for example, soil conservation measures which provide intrinsic incentives for land users;
□    research into the underlying causes of degradation, and the integration of land resource management with wider aspects of population policy.

**Proposal 6    Implementation of measures to combat the direct causes of degradation.**

Much activity of this nature is already being undertaken, but the scale of activity needs to be expanded. Increased funding will be required. Measures of this type include:

□    watershed management and soil conservation projects and extension work;
□    method for improving soil organic matter status;
□    application of integrated plant nutrition systems;
□    salinity control and reclamation projects;
□    reafforestation;
□    further development of agroforestry, including applications for soil conservation;
□    control of desertification, including sand dune fixation and improved rangeland management.

**Proposal 7    Action directed towards removing the underlying causes of degradation, including integration of land management measures with population policy.**

Attempts to combat land degradation directly, by conservation measures or land reclamation, can have only short-term effects unless they are accompanied by efforts to tackle the underlying causes. These lie in the causal nexus between population increase, limited land resources, land shortage, poverty, non-sustainable management practices and land degradation. In the prevailing situation in which there is no spare land available, population increases of 2-3 percent per year will largely or entirely counteract the effects of measures for improvement.

Population is a sensitive issue, but all governments of the region are aware of the problems caused by continued increase at present rates. In the context of land degradation, a much greater integration between population policy, agriculture and land resource management is needed. For this to occur, new attitudes will be required.

# References

Abrol, I.P. 1990. Problem soils in India. In: *Problem Soils of Asia and the Pacific* (FAO/RAPA, Bangkok). pp. 153-65.

Afghanistan, Ministry of Planning. 1992. Afghanistan: the transition from war to rehabilitation and development. *Report to UNCED*. Ministry of Planning, Kabul, 131 pp.

Ahmad Y.J., El Serafy, S. and Lutz, E. (eds.). 1989. *Environmental Accounting for Sustainable Development*. World Bank, Washington DC, 100 pp.

Ahmad, M. and Kutcher, G.P. 1992. Irrigation planning with environmental considerations: a case study of Pakistan's Indus basin. *World Bank Technical Paper 166*. World Bank, Washington DC, 196 pp.

Asian Development Bank. 1990. *Economic Policies for Sustainable Development*. Asian Development Bank, Manila, 253 pp.

Asian Development Bank. 1991. Population pressure and natural resources management: key issues and possible actions. *ADB Environment Paper 6*. Asian Development Bank, Manila, 40 pp.

Asian Development Bank. 1992a. *Pakistan: Forestry Sector Master Plan. Upland degraded Watershed Component*. Asian Development Bank, Manila.

Asian Development Bank. 1992b. *Forest Cover/Land Use Maps of Pakistan. 1:250 000*. Asian Development Bank, Manila.

Banerjee, A. and Grimes, A. in press. *Rehabilitation of Degraded Forests in Asia*. World Bank, Asia Technical Department.

Bangladesh. 1992. *Land Degradation*. Paper presented to FAO 21st Regional Conference for Asia and the Pacific, New Delhi.

Bhutan, National Environmental Secretariat. 1992. *Bhutan: Towards Sustainable Development in a Unique Environment*. National Environmental Secretariat, Thimphu, 71 pp.

Biswas, A. and Tewatia, R.K. 1991. Nutrient balance in agro-climatic regions of India - an overview. *Fert. News* 36(6): 13-18.

Bojo, J. 1992. Cost-benefit analysis of soil and water conservation projects: a review of 20 empirical studies. In: *Soil Conservation for Survival*. Kebebe Tato and H. Hurni (eds.). Soil and Water Conservation Society, Ankeny, Iowa. pp. 195-205.

Bowonder, B.. 1981. The myth and reality of high yield varieties in Indian agriculture. *Development and Change* 12 (20).

Castro, C. 1991. *Upland Conservation in Asia and the Pacific*. FAO/RAPA, Bangkok. 114 pp.

Chaudhary, M.K. and Aneja, D.R. 1991. Impact of green revolution on long-term sustainability of land and water resources in Harayana. *Indian Journal of Agricultural Economics* 45: 428-32.

Chisholm, A. and Dumsday, R. (eds.). 1987. *Land Degradation: Problems and Policies*. Cambridge University Press, Cambridge, UK. 404 pp.

Chopra, H. 1989. Land degradation: dimensions and casualties. *Indian Journal of Agricultural Economics* 44: 45-54.

Cruz, W. and Repetto, R. 1992. *The Environmental Effects of Stabilization and Structural Adjustment Programs: The Philippines Case*. World Resources Institute, Washington DC. 90 pp.

Das, D.C. 1977. Soil conservation practices and erosion control in India - a case study. *FAO Soils Bulletin 33*. FAO, Rome. pp. 11-50.

Das, D.C., Dhuruvanarayana, V.V. and Sarkar, T.K. 1991. Soil-related constraints in crop production - soil erosion. *Bull. No. 15, Indian Soc. Soil Sci.*, New Delhi. pp. 14-26.

Dent, F.J. 1992. Environmental issues in land and water development - a regional perspective. In: *FAO/RAPA, Environmental Issues in Land and Water Development*. FAO/RAPA, Bangkok. pp. 52-74.

Dent, F.J., Rao, Y.S. and Takeuchi, K. 1992. *Regional Strategies for Arresting Land Degradation ("Womb of the Earth")*. FAO/RAPA, Bangkok, 26 pp.

Doolette, J.B. and Magrath, W.B. (eds.). 1990. Watershed development in Asia: strategies and technologies. *World Bank Technical Paper 127*. World Bank, Washington DC. 227 pp.

Environmental Resources Limited. 1988. *Natural Resource Management for Sustainable Development: A Study of Feasible Policies, Institutions and Investment Activities in Nepal with special emphasis on the hills*. Environmental Resources Limited for the World Bank, London, 228 pp.

ESCAP. 1983. *Problems and Prospects of Desertification Control in the ESCAP Region*. ESCAP/UNEP, Bangkok. 372 pp.

ESCAP. 1986. *Environmental and Socio-economic Aspects of Tropical Deforestation in Asia and the Pacific*. ESCAP, Bangkok. 142 pp.

ESCAP. 1987a. Population policies and programmes. Current status and future directions. *Asian Population Studies 84*. UN, New York. 216 pp.

ESCAP. 1987b. *Desertification in Asia and the Pacific: A Regional Review and Assessment*. ESCAP, Bangkok.

ESCAP. 1989a. Consequences of population growth in Asia: a methodological guideline. *Asia Population Studies 102*. ESCAP, Bangkok. 154 pp.

ESCAP. 1989b. *Desertification in Indus Basin due to Salinity and Waterlogging: A Case Study.* ESCAP, Bangkok. 57 pp.

ESCAP. 1990a. *State of the Environment in Asia and the Pacific.* ESCAP, Bangkok. 352 pp.

ESCAP. 1990b. *Waterlogging and Salinity Control in Asia and the Pacific.* ESCAP, Bangkok. 61 pp.

ESCAP. 1991a. Economic and Social Commission for Asia and the Pacific. *Annual Report, June 1990 - April 1991.* UN, New York. 176 pp.

ESCAP. 1991b. *Desertification through Wind Erosion and its Control in Asia and the Pacific.* UN, New York. 139 pp.

FAO. 1976. A framework for land evaluation. *FAO Soils Bulletin 32.* FAO, Rome.

FAO. 1979. *A Provisional Methodology for Soil Degradation Assessment.* FAO, Rome, 73 pp.

FAO. 1978-80. Report on Agro-ecological zones project. Vol. 2 (1978). Results for southwest Asia. Vol. 4 (1980). Results for southeast Asia. *World Soil Resources Report 48/2 and 48/4.* FAO, Rome. 28 and 41 pp.

FAO. 1982. *Population Supporting Capacities of Lands in the Developing World.* FAO, Rome 139 pp. plus maps.

FAO. 1986a. Watershed management in Asia and the Pacific: needs and opportunities for action. *Technical Report FO:RAS/85/017.* FAO, Rome. 166 pp.

FAO. 1986b. Status report on plant nutrition in fertilizer programmes countries in Asia and Pacific region. *AGL/MISC/86/7.* FAO, Rome.

FAO. 1988. Nepal: integrated watershed management, torrent control and land use development. *FO:DP/NEP/74/020.* UNDP/FAO, Rome. 44 pp.

FAO. 1991. *Network on Erosion-induced Loss in Soil Productivity.* FAO, Rome. 52 pp.

FAO. 1992. *The State of Food and Agriculture 1991.* FAO, Rome. 228 pp.

FAO. 1992. Findings and recommendations for the tropical zone. *Forest Resources Assessment 1990 Project.* FAO, Rome 30 pp.

FAO/RAPA. 1986. *Land Use Watersheds, and Planning in the Asia-Pacific Region.* FAO/RAPA, Bangkok. 230 pp.

FAO/RAPA. 1990. Problem soils of Asia and the Pacific. *RAPA Report 1990/6.* FAO/RAPA Bangkok. 283 pp.

FAO/RAPA. 1991. Organic recycling in Asia and the Pacific. *RAPA Bulletin 7.* FAO/RAPA, Bangkok. 112 pp.

FAO/RAPA. 1992. *Environmental Issues in Land and Water Development.* FAO/RAPA, Bangkok. 488 pp. (Includes country papers on Bangladesh, India, Nepal, Pakistan and Sri Lanka.)

Goswami, N.N. and Rattan, R.K. 1992. Soil health - key to sustained agricultural productivity. *Fertilizer News [India]*. pp. 53-60.

Hutchinson C.F. and Webb, A.C. 1987. *United States-Pakistan Workshop on Arid Lands Development and Desertification Control*. Pakistan Agricultural Research Council, Islamabad. 235 pp.

Joshi, P.K. and Tyagi, N.K. 1991. Sustainability of existing farming system in Punjab and Harayana - some issues on groundwater use. *Indian Journal of Agricultural Economics* 46: 412-21.

Joshi, P.K. and Jha, D. 1992. An economic enquiry into the impact of soil alkalinity and waterlogging. *Indian Journal of Agricultural Economics* 47: 195-204.

Kholdebarin A. 1992. *Desertification and its Control in the Islamic Republic of Iran*. Forestry and Range Organization, Teheran. 48 pp.

Lutz, E. and El Serafy, S. 1988. Environmental and resource accounting: an overview. *Environment Department Working Paper 6*. World Bank, Washington DC. 14 pp.

Magrath, W.B. 1989. Economic analysis of soil conservation technologies. *Environment Department, Division Working Paper 1989-4*. World Bank, Washington DC. 28 pp.

Magrath, W.[B.] and Arens, P. 1989. The costs of soil erosion on Java: a natural resource accounting approach. *Environment Department Working Paper 18*. World Bank, Washington DC. 67 pp.

Magrath, W.B. and Doolette, J.B. 1990. Strategic issues for watershed development in Asia. *Environment Working Paper 30*. World Bank, Washington DC. 34 pp.

Mellink, W., Rao, Y.S. and MacDicken, KG. (eds.). 1991. *Agroforestry in Asia and the Pacific*. RAPA, Bangkok. 304 pp.

Mian, A. and Javed. Y. 1989. *The Soil Resources of Pakistan - Their Potential, Present State and Strategies for Conservation*. Sector paper of the National Conservation Strategy. Soil Survey of Pakistan, Lahore. 53 pp.

Nizami, M.I. and Shafiq, M. 1990. Land clearances and soil conservation. A case study of Pothwar Plateau. *Proceedings of the 2nd National Soils Congress of Pakistan (Soil Science Society of Pakistan, Islamabad)*. pp. 162-69.

Noohi, K. 1992. *Drought and Desertification. Report of Working Group on Agricultural Meteorology*. Paper presented to meeting on elaboration of desertification assessment and mapping methodology, November 1992, Teheran. Meteorological Organization, Teheran. 43 pp.

Oldeman, L.R., Hakkeling, A.T.A. and Sombroek, W.G. 1992. *World Map of the Status of Human-induced Soil Degradation*. ISRIC, Wageningen and UNEP, Nairobi. 26 pp. with map in 3 sheets.

Parikh, K.S., Parikh, J.K., Sharma, V.K. and Painuly, J.P. 1992. *Natural Resource Accounting: A Framework for India*. Indira Ghandi Institute of Development Research, Bombay.

Pearce, D.W. and Turner, R.K. 1990. *Economics of Natural Resources and the Environment*. Johns Hopkins, Baltimore. 378 pp.

Peskin, H.M. 1990. Accounting for natural resource depletion and degradation in developing countries. *Environment Department Working Paper 13*. World Bank, Washington DC. 39 pp.

Pezzey, J. 1992. Sustainable development concepts: an economic analysis. *Environment Paper 2*. World Bank, Washington DC. 71 pp.

Pradhan, S.B. 1992. *Status of Fertilizer Use in the [Asia-Pacific] Region*. Paper presented to FADINAP seminar, Fertilization and the environment, Chiang Mai, Thailand.

Repetto, R., Magrath, W., Wells, M., Beer, C. and Rossini, F. 1989. *Wasting Assets: Natural Resources in the National Income Accounts*. World Resources Institute, Washington DC, 68 pp.

SAARC. 1992. *Regional Study on the Causes and Consequences of Natural Disasters and the Protection and Preservation of the Environment*. South Asia Association for Regional Cooperation, Kathmandu. 212 pp.

Salleh Modh. Nor. 1992. Forestry research in the Asia-Pacific. *FORSPA Publication: 1*, FAO/UNDP/ADB/CAB International, Bangkok. 55 pp.

Saunders, I. and Young, A. 1983. Rates of surface processes on slopes, slope retreat and denudation. *Earth Surface Processes and landform* 8: 473-501.

Schertz, D.L. 1983. The basis for soil loss tolerances. *Journal of Soil and Water Conservation* 38: 10-14.

Sehgal, J. and Abrol, I. P. 1992. Land degradation status: India. *Desertification Bulletin* 21: 24-31.

Shaheed, S.M. 1992. Environmental issues in land development in Bangladesh. In: *Environmental Issues in Land and Water Development*. FAO/RAPA, Bangkok. pp. 105-27.

Singh, B. 1992. Groundwater resources and agricultural development strategy: Punjab experience. *Indian Journal of Agricultural Economics* 47: 105-13.

Sing, P. 1988. *Indian Rangelands: Status and Improvement*. Plenary address, Third International Rangeland Congress, New Delhi. 40 pp.

Sinha, R. 1984. Landlessness: a growing problem. *FAO Economic and Social Development Studies 28*. FAO, Rome. 112 pp.

Southgate, D. 1989. The economics of land degradation in the third world. *Environment Department Working Paper 2*. World Bank, Washington DC. 17 pp.

Sri Lanka, Natural Resources, Energy and Science Authority. 1991. *Natural Resources of Sri Lanka: Conditions and Trends*. Natural Resources, Energy and Science Authority, Colombo. 280 pp.

Sri Lanka, Ministry of Environment and Parliamentary Affairs. 1991. *National Environmental Action Plan*. Ministry of Environment and Parliamentary Affairs. 100 pp.

Stocking, M. 1986. The cost of soil erosion in Zimbabwe in terms of the loss of three major nutrients. *Consultants' Working Paper 3*. AGLS, FAO, Rome. 164 pp.

Stocking, M. 1992. Soil erosion in the upper Mahaweli catchment. *Technical Report 14*, Forests/Landuse Mapping Project. Mahaweli Authority of Sri Lanka, Polgolla. 56 pp.

Sun, P. (ed.). 1989. Land and water resource management in Asia. *EDI Seminar Report 20*. Economic Development Institute of the World Bank, Washington DC. 64 pp.

Tandon, H.L.S. 1992. *Assessment of Soil Nutrient Depletion*. Paper presented to FADINAP seminar, Fertilization and the environment, Chiang Mai, Thailand.

Twyford, I. 1994. *Fertilizer Use and Crop Yields*. Paper presented to 4th National Congress of the Soil Science Society of Pakistan, Islamabad. 1992.

UNEP. 1977. *World Map of Desertification, at a scale of 1:25 000 000*. FAO/UNEP/WMO/, Nairobi.

UNEP. 1992a. *World Atlas of Desertification*. Arnold, London. 69 pp.

UNEP. 1992b. Desertification, land degradation [definitions]. *Desertification Control Bulletin 21*.

Vittal, K.P.R., Vijayalakshmi, K. and Rao, U.M.B. 1990. The effect of cumulative erosion and rainfall on sorghum, pearl millet and castor bean yields under dry farming conditions in Andhra Pradesh, India. *Experimental Agriculture* 26: 429-39.

World Bank. 1989. *Philippines: Environment and Natural Resource Management Study*. World Bank, Washington DC. 170 pp.

World Bank. 1991. Bangladesh: Environment strategy review. *Report 9551-BD*. World Bank, Washington DC. 73 pp.

World Bank. 1992. *World Development Report 1992: Development and the Environment*. Oxford University Press, Oxford, for World Bank, Washington DC. 308 pp.

World Resources Institute. 1992. *1993 Directory of Country Environmental Studies*. World Resources Institute, Washington DC. 230 pp.

Yadav, J.S.P. 1993. Land degradation in South Asia. *Consultant's Report, RAS/92/560*. FAO/RAPA, Bangkok.

Young, A. 1985. Common sense about desertification? *Soil Survey and Land Evaluation* 4: 90-91.

Young, A. 1989. *Agroforestry for Soil Conservation*. CAB International, Wallingford, UK and ICRAF, Nairobi. 276 pp.

Young, A. 1991. Soil monitoring: a basic task for soil survey organizations. *Soil Use and Management* 7: 126-30.

Young, A. 1992. *Land Degradation in South Asia, its Severity, Causes, and Effects upon the People* (according to ECOSOC Resolution 1991/97). Final Report. UNDP/FAO/UNEP, Rome. 23 pp.

## WORLD SOIL RESOURCES REPORTS

1. Report of the First Meeting of the Advisory Panel on the Soil Map of the World, Rome, 19-23 June 1961.**

2. Report of the First Meeting on Soil Survey, Correlation and Interpretation for Latin America, Rio de Janeiro, Brazil, 28-31 May 1962**

3. Report of the First Soil Correlation Seminar for Europe, Moscow, USSR, 16-28 July 1962.**

4. Report of the First Soil Correlation Seminar for South and Central Asia, Tashkent, Uzbekistan, USSR, 14 September-2 October 1962.**

5. Report of the Fourth Session of the Working Party on Soil Classification and Survey (Subcommission on Land and Water Use of the European Commission on Agriculture), Lisbon, Portugal, 6-10 March 1963.**

6. Report of the Second Meeting of the Advisory Panel on the Soil Map of the World, Rome, 9-11 July 1963.**

7. Report of the Second Soil Correlation Seminar for Europe, Bucharest, Romania, 29 July-6 August 1963.**

8. Report of the Third Meeting of the Advisory Panel on the Soil Map of the World, Paris, 3 January 1964.**

9. Adequacy of Soil Studies in Paraguay, Bolivia and Peru, November-December 1963.**

10. Report on the Soils of Bolivia, January 1964.**

11. Report on the Soils of Paraguay, January 1964.**

12. Preliminary Definition, Legend and Correlation Table for the Soil Map of the World, Rome, August 1964.**

13. Report of the Fourth Meeting of the Advisory Panel on the Soil Map of the World, Rome, 16-21 May 1964.**

14. Report of the Meeting on the Classification and Correlation of Soils from Volcanic Ash, Tokyo, Japan, 11-27 June 1964.**

15. Report of the First Session of the Working Party on Soil Classification, Survey and Soil Resources of the European Commission on Agriculture, Florence, Italy, 1-3 October 1964.**

16. Detailed Legend for the Third Draft on the Soil Map of South America, June 1965.**

17. Report of the First Meeting on Soil Correlation for North America, Mexico, 1-8 February 1965.**

18. The Soil Resources of Latin America, October 1965.**

19. Report of the Third Correlation Seminar for Europe: Bulgaria, Greece, Romania, Turkey, Yugoslavia, 29 August-22 September 1965.**

20. Report of the Meeting of Rapporteurs, Soil Map of Europe (Scale 1:1 000 000) (Working Party on Soil Classification and Survey of the European Commission on Agriculture), Bonn, Federal Republic of Germany, 29 November-3 December 1965.**

21. Report of the Second Meeting on Soil Survey, Correlation and Interpretation for Latin America, Rio de Janeiro, Brazil, 13-16 July 1965.**

22. Report of the Soil Resources Expedition in Western and Central Brazil, 24 June-9 July 1965.**

23. Bibliography on Soils and Related Sciences for Latin America (1st edition), December 1965.**

24. Report on the Soils of Paraguay (2nd edition), August 1964.**

25. Report of the Soil Correlation Study Tour in Uruguay, Brazil and Argentina, June-August 1964.**

26. Report of the Meeting on Soil Correlation and Soil Resources Appraisal in India, New Delhi, India, 5-15 April 1965.**

27. Report of the Sixth Session of the Working Party on Soil Classification and Survey of the European Commission on Agriculture, Montpellier, France, 7-11 March 1967.**

28. Report of the Second Meeting on Soil Correlation for North America, Winnipeg-Vancouver, Canada, 25 July-5 August 1966.**

29. Report of the Fifth Meeting of the Advisory Panel on the Soil Map of the World, Moscow, USSR, 20-28 August 1966.**

30. Report of the Meeting of the Soil Correlation Committee for South America, Buenos Aires, Argentina, 12-19 December 1966.**

31. Trace Element Problems in Relation to Soil Units in Europe (Working Party on Soil Classification and Survey of the European Commission on Agriculture), Rome, 1967.**

32. Approaches to Soil Classification, 1968.**

33. Definitions of Soil Units for the Soil Map of the World, April 1968.**
34. Soil Map of South America 1:5 000 000, Draft Explanatory Text, November 1968.**
35. Report of a Soil Correlation Study Tour in Sweden and Poland, 27 September-14 October 1968.**
36. Meeting of Rapporteurs, Soil Map of Europe (Scale 1:1 000 000) (Working Party on Soil Classification and Survey of the European Commission on Agriculture), Poitiers, France 21-23 June 1967.**
37. Supplement to Definition of Soil Units for the Soil Map of the World, July 1969.**
38. Seventh Session of the Working Party on Soil Classification and Survey of the European Commission on Agriculture, Varna, Bulgaria, 11-13 September 1969.**
39. A Correlation Study of Red and Yellow Soils in Areas with a Mediterranean Climate.**
40. Report of the Regional Seminar of the Evaluation of Soil Resources in West Africa, Kumasi, Ghana, 14-19 December 1970.**
41. Soil Survey and Soil Fertility Research in Asia and the Far East, New Delhi, 15-20 February 1971.**
42. Report of the Eighth Session of the Working Party on Soil Classification and Survey of the European Commission on Agriculture, Helsinki, Finland, 5-7 July 1971.**
43. Report of the Ninth Session of the Working Party on Soil Classification and Survey of the European Commission on Agriculture, Ghent, Belgium 28-31 August 1973.**
44. First Meeting of the West African Sub-Committee on Soil Correlation for Soil Evaluation and Management, Accra, Ghana, 12-19 June 1972.**
45. Report of the Ad Hoc Expert Consultation on Land Evaluation, Rome, Italy, 6-8 January 1975.**
46. First Meeting of the Eastern African Sub-Committee for Soil Correlation and Land Evaluation, Nairobi, Kenya, 11-16 March 1974.**
47. Second Meeting of the Eastern African Sub-Committee for Soil Correlation and Land Evaluation, Addis Ababa, Ethiopia, 25-30 October 1976.
48. Report on the Agro-Ecological Zones Project, Vol. 1 - Methodology and Results for Africa, 1978. Vol. 2 - Results for Southwest Asia, 1978.
49. Report of an Expert Consultation on Land Evaluation Standards for Rainfed Agriculture, Rome, Italy, 25-28 October 1977.
50. Report of an Expert Consultation on Land Evaluation Criteria for Irrigation, Rome, Italy, 27 February-2 March 1979.
51. Third Meeting of the Eastern African Sub-Committee for Soil Correlation and Land Evaluation, Lusaka, Zambia, 18-30 April 1978.
52. Land Evaluation Guidelines for Rainfed Agriculture, Report of an Expert Consultation, 12-14 December 1979.
53. Fourth Meeting of the West African Sub-Committee for Soil Correlation and Land Evaluation, Banjul, The Gambia, 20-27 October 1979.
54. Fourth Meeting of the Eastern African Sub-Committee for Soil Correlation and Land Evaluation, Arusha, Tanzania, 27 October-4 November 1980.
55. Cinquième réunion du Sous-Comité Ouest et Centre africain de corrélation des sols pour la mise en valeur des terres, Lomé, Togo, 7-12 décembre 1981.
56. Fifth Meeting of the Eastern African Sub-Committee for Soil Correlation and Land Evaluation, Wad Medani, Sudan, 5-10 December 1983.
57. Sixième réunion du Sous-Comité Ouest et Centre Africain de corrélation des sols pour la mise en valeur des terres, Niamey, Niger, 6-12 février 1984.
58. Sixth Meeting of the Eastern African Sub-Committee for Soil Correlation and Land Evaluation, Maseru, Lesotho, 9-18 October 1985.
59. Septième réunion du Sous-Comité Ouest et Centre africain de corrélation des sols pour la mise en valeur des terres, Ouagadougou, Burkina Faso, 10-17 novembre 1985.
60. Revised Legend, Soil Map of the World, FAO-Unesco-ISRIC, 1988. Reprinted 1990.
61. Huitième réunion du Sous-Comité Ouest et Centre africain de corrélation des sols pour la mise en valeur des terres, Yaoundé, Cameroun, 19-28 janvier 1987.
62. Seventh Meeting of the East and Southern African Sub-Committee for Soil Correlation and Evaluation, Gaborone, Botswana, 30 March-8 April 1987.
63. Neuvième réunion du Sous-Comité Ouest et Centre africain de corrélation des sols pour la mise en valeur des terres, Cotonou, Bénin, 14-23 novembre 1988.

64.     FAO-ISRIC Soil Database (SDB), 1989.

65.     Eighth Meeting of the East and Southern African Sub-Committee for Soil Correlation and Land Evaluation, Harare, Zimbabwe, 9-13 October 1989.

66.     World soil resources. An explanatory note on the FAO World Soil Resources Map at 1:25 000 000 scale, 1991. Rev. 1, 1993.

67.     Digitized Soil Map of the World, Volume 1: Africa. Volume 2: North and Central America. Volume 3: Central and South America. Volume 4: Europe and West of the Urals. Volume 5: North East Asia. Volume 6: Near East and Far East. Volume 7: South East Asia and Oceania. Release 1.0, November 1991.

68.     Land Use Planning Applications. Proceedings of the FAO Expert Consultation 1990, Rome, 10-14 December 1990.

69.     Dixième réunion du Sous-Comité Ouest et Centre africain de corrélation des sols pour la mise en valeur des terres, Bouaké, Odienné, Côte d'Ivoire, Côte d'Ivoire, 5-12 november 1990.

70.     Ninth Meeting of the East and Southern African Sub-Committee for Soil Correlation and Land Evaluation, Lilongwe, Malawi, 25 November - 2 December 1991.

71.     Agro-ecological land resources assessment for agricultural development planning. A case study of Kenya. Resources data base and land productivity. Main Report. Technical Annex 1: Land resources. Technical Annex 2: Soil erosion and productivity. Technical Annex 3: Agro-climatic and agro-edaphic suitabilities for barley, oat, cowpea, green gram and pigeonpea. Technical Annex 4: Crop productivity. Technical Annex 5: Livestock productivity. Technical Annex 6: Fuelwood productivity. Technical Annex 7: Systems documentation guide to computer programs for land productivity assessments. Technical Annex 8: Crop productivity assessment: results at district level. 1991. Main Report 71/9: Making land use choices for district planning, 1994.

72.     Computerized systems of land resources appraisal for agricultural development, 1993.

73.     FESLM: an international framework for evaluating sustainable land management, 1993.

74.     Global and national soils and terrain digital databases (SOTER), 1993.

75.     AEZ in Asia. Proceedings of the Regional Workshop on Agro-ecological Zones Methodology and Applications, Bangkok, Thailand, 17-23 November 1991.

76.     Green manuring for soil productivity improvement, 1994.

77.     Onzième réunion du Sous-Comité Ouest et Centre africain de corrélation des sols pour la mise en valeur des terres, Ségou, Mali, 18-26 janvier 1993.

78.     Land degradation in South Asia: its severity, causes and effects upon the people, 1994.

** \*\***     Out of print